ST. PANCREAS DEFENDERS

'The Bone Letter'

MICHAEL ROSEN

ILLUSTRATED BY
ZOOM ROCKMAN AND JOHN LIGHTBOURNE

Seven Arches
Publishing

Published in 2022
By Seven Arches Publishing
The Flat, New Inn Farm Beckley, Oxford, OX3 9TY
www.sevenarchespublishing.co.uk

Seven Arches

Publishing

Cover design and typesetting by Alan McGlynn

Printed in Great Britain

ISBN 978-0-9567572-7-2

Michael Rosen has written at least 90 books including:

Many Different Kinds of Love
A story of life, death and the NHS
(Currently a Sunday Times Best Seller)

So They Call You Pisher! A Memoir

The Missing - The True Story of My Family in World War II

Michael Rosen's Sad Book

Chocolate Cake

The Laugh Out Loud Joke Book

We're Going on a Bear Hunt

You Wait Till I'm Older than You

When Boris Johnson became prime minister in July 2019, Flett, Esq. received letters from Jacob Rees Mogg coming from Michael Rosen's twitter account. It was a bit of fun to express shared exasperation at the turn of events. The numbers of 'likes' and 'retweets' was relatively few, at first.

However, with ever-increasing wit, humour and undeniable vulgarity the tweets, now addressed to Boris and others in government began to reflect not only the absurdity but also the tragedy of many governmental decisions. Followers, likes and retweets increased accordingly. Many began commenting themselves in a similar vein, thus creating a new twitter thread. Some simply said 'Thank you. You have made me laugh when I felt like crying."

With Michael Rosen's special interest in education and schools, it is hardly surprising that many of the most 'liked' tweets were ones about Gavin Wiliamson, the Minister for Education during the pandemic and lockdown.

In August 2022, the author was telling his followers on Facebook about his 'Dear Boris' tweets. He copied and pasted a few to give an idea of what they were like. Some of the words used got him in to trouble with the 'guardians of free speech' on Facebook. They gave him a three day suspension and 'multiple restrictions' once his suspension was over.

for all those resisting the onslaught

*The observant reader will notice the months of this year when there were no letters from Boris or anyone else. This is because the author had Covid-19 and was in an ICU in an NHS hospital.

PART 1 2018 – 2019

THROUGH THE DOOR OF NUMBER 10 DOWNING STREET

In scrotum credo
(and getting Brexit done)

In March 2018 Boris Johnson was Foreign Secretary in Theresa May's government.

Mar 22, 2018

Dear Boris Johnson,
Can your next Tory party fund-raising tennis match with oligarchs and/or their partners/relations etc be in public on high ground. Moral high ground, that is.
Yours, Secret Admirer.

Mar 22, 2018

Dear Boris Johnson,
Now you have done the Hitler 1936 thing (loved it!) can
you move on to doing a tasteful riff on 'nerve gas' and
'gas chambers'?
Best wishes,
Your Number One Fan.

Apr 6, 2018

Dear Theresa,
My great poem, 'Rouble Yarn' (in the style of Coleridge's
'Kubla Khan') is unfinished as I was interrupted in full
flow by the Person from Porton, whom, sadly, I have
been unable to trace.
Salutations, Boris.

**In October 2018 Boris Johnson resigned as Foreign Secretary.
In the spring and early summer of 2019, despite May's slogan
of 'Brexit means Brexit' her bills to action Brexit put forward to
parliament were failing to go through.**

**Theresa May offered her resignation to the Queen on the
23rd July. After defeating others in the contest for leadership
of the conservative party, Boris Johnson became prime minister.**

Jul 28, 2019

Dear Flett esq.,
Boris has emerged from the bedroom with an actress
familiar to some, I gather. He says he has never seen the
child before in his life. Cummings says we won't need
children in the future.
Yours in flagrante tremens,
Jacob Police-Dogg

Dear Flett esq.,
Goldsmith, Dorries and Cummings are tramping round
the tent with forks from the dining-set held aloft
chanting, 'Go home Muslims!' which is discomforting
Javid somewhat. Boris is in the bedroom with someone.
Yours in coitus cumulus,
Jacob Sleaze-Frog

Dear Flett esq.,
Cummings says our next step should be to
denationalise the army. Boris has fallen asleep on his
arms on the Cabinet Table. I have texted my wife to
move more of our savings to the Caymans.
Yours in sanitas insanitatis,
Jacob Loose-Cog

Dear Flett Esq.
Tomorrow, Toby Young, Douglas Murray, James
Delingpole, Roger Scruton and I will make the case to
Boris that following Brexit on November 1, we will
abolish the egregiously French accent on the 'e' in the
word 'cafe'.
Yours in anus horribilis,
Jacob Real-Legg

Dear Flett esq.,
I caught sight of Boris trying on a kilt. I was able to
convince him not to wear it for his jaunt to the
Hebrides.Will he tame the Pictish heathens and

Calvinists? They need reminding that they use English currency up there.
Yours in testes absentia,
Jacob Right-Egg

Dear Flett, Esq.,
Douglas Murray has been explaining that the Paddies
were forerunners to the Muslims in the downfall of
Europe. Ireland has become a foreign country, he says. I
hope Boris makes these points when he goes there.
Yours in vomitarium,
Jacob Scheiss-Gobb

**At this time the conservatives have a very small majority. They
needed to start canvassing for support in the country. No
general election had yet been called. It is getting near to the
summer recess for parliament.**

Dear Flett esq.,
Dominic Cummings has a map of Britain in the war tent
in Number 10 and he's been showing Boris where the
'countryside' is, then stabbing his swagger stick at green
bits, saying 'Go there Boris and tell'em you love'em.'
Yours in porcus porcorom,
Jacob Lease-Pigg

Dear Flett Esq.,
Cummings says we should build a wall round the British
Isles and ask the EU to pay for it. This is a reasonable
proposition, and I will put this to Boris when he comes
back from the Welsh dung-heap he is trapped in today.
Yours in Hadriani,
Jacob Keep-Out

In Boris Johnson's new cabinet, Gavin Williamson is Secretary for Education.

Jul 30, 2019

Dear Flett Esq.,
Nick Gibb is in to explain phonics to Williamson. I'm very impressed by the idea children are learning to read without understanding what they're reading. Boris may need people in that situation for the election.
Yours in commandat populatio,
Jacob Tells-Plebs

Jul 30, 2019

Dear Flett Esq.,
I am urging Boris to use images of Richard Branson with a slogan: 'With the Conservatives, anyone can be a Branson...not everyone, because we need the servants...and not anyone in actual fact, but you see what we mean.'
Yours in cranium zero,
Jacob Speak-dung

Jul 30, 2019

Dear Flett Esq.,
Dominic Cummings has just burst out of his HQ tent waving his swagger stick, shouting, 'Boris! Say that the EU are Brexiting us!' Boris was playing on the Game Boy his mummy sent him at Eton but I think he got the message.
In culpa europa,
Jacob Please-Dog

Jul 31, 2019

Dear Flett Esq.,
I fear Boris may make a faux pas during his trip to Ulster
today. Just before he left, he grabbed me by the arm,
saying, 'The Orange Order are the good guys, right?'
'Yes,' I said, 'but we don't say it anymore.'
Yours in crisis permanens,
Jacurb Green-Lot

Jul 31, 2019

Dear Flett Esq.,
Herewith a letter for Boris to take to France. I fear my
French is not as good as it was at Eton. 'Monsoor
Macron, Nous somme vomit et fatigué avec vous. Vous
pouvez jumper dans un lac. Allons coopéreration!'
Yours in Gaul Caesar vincit,
Jacob Lost-Bogg

Jul 31, 2019

Dear Flett Esq.,
Boris is telling the EU what to do. He is so imperious,
single-minded, powerful, authoritative, masterful,
decisive and manly. Let's see now how the EU come
grovelling and snivelling, begging the mighty lion to
relent.
Yours in Albion superbus,
Jacob Rash-God

Aug 11, 2019

Dear all in the cabinet,
Through the summer pump out supercharged positive
stuff about anything that comes into your head.
Best,
Boris

Aug 24, 2019

Dear Ireland,
You've been having a laugh doing your own thing for
long enough. Shape up, time's up, you're coming back to
Great Britain. Border biz solved!
Maximus cerebellum habeo,
Boris

Aug 24, 2019

Dear Nicola,
I've been to Scotland. Very jolly people you have up
there. After Brexit, you can be just as jolly.
Notwithstanding nevertheless insofar as albeit.
Non desperandum in faeces omnibus,
Boris

**The summer recess of parliament is still on-going. The inner
circle of the government has decided to request the prorogation
of parliament. Only the Queen can give consent for this. There
must be a reason given for the request. It provides for the temporary closure of parliament.**

Aug 24, 2019

Dear Elizabeth,
Very soon I may be calling on you to wangle a little jobby
I've got to bring to a conclusion. Can I ask you to take no
notice of the unpleasant Levantine Bercow on this
matter?
Honi soit qui mal y ponce,
Boris

Aug 24, 2019

Dear Geoff,
Need a bit of legal howzyerfather from you, dear boy. I
can blooming well shut the door to the House, can't I?
Cheque in the post.
Gaudeamus in toto blotto,
Boris

Aug 25, 2019

Dear Donald,
May I first say how much I admire your wonderfully
forthright, truthful, insightful approach to politics, your
beautiful wife, and your extraordinarily talented children
and their spouses? Can we have a trade deal?
Non Sparta sed Tesco,
Boris

**Jo Swinson became the leader of the Liberal Democratic party.
She made it clear that she was not interested in setting up an
alliance with the leader of the Labour party, Jeremy Corbyn at
any possible by-elections in order to defeat the Conservative.**

Aug 25, 2019

Dear Jo,
Assured dear girl, I'm watching from the sidelines and
very much enjoying your refusal to work with the
frightful Corbyn. Alliances in the future are not
impossible. ...wink wink.
Non sequitur mea culpa,
Boris

Dear Theresa,
Hope you're well and enjoying the cricket. You know that lash-up deal you ran past us? Any chance I could purloin it? I have a little scheme involving its use.
Semper fidelis in post partum,
Boris

At this time John Bercow, a labour MP, is the Speaker in the House of Commons. The Speaker's role is to ensure that there is a fair distribution of time between the different parties and persons and that 'order' is maintained.

Dear John,
As you're the Speaker I'm pretty darned sure you've got the keys for the House, in which case jolly well hand them over in case I need to lock up.
In dulci jubilo mama mia,
Boris

Dear Nigel,
Have you seen the Corbyn conspiracy lined up against me? I will need your assistance as we reach port as well as our Stone Age pals from Belfast. All hands on deck!
Ad hoc in hoc,
Boris

Gavin Williamson is the Education Secretary. The Conservative's plan for education at this time was controversial because of several factors, one being greater powers for excluding pupils who have misbehaved.

Aug 28, 2019

Dear Gavin,
The bloody Guardianistas have leaked our education
plans. Keep your nerve: they're spiffing. Best bit: the
crackdown on behaviour and exclusions. Mind you, I'd
have come a cropper if it had been applied to me when I
was that age!!!
Rictus rectum nasturtium,
Boris

Aug 28, 2019

Dear Boris,
Sorry I don't understand the Latin. We should discuss
making it compulsory. Sorry about the leek. Sorry, I
mean leak. It wasn't me. I think we should headline with
'Knife Crime' and 'Exclusions'. Get the criminals out of
schools, make streets safe.
Best,
Gavin

Charles II was beheaded in 1649.

Aug 28, 2019

Dear Elizabeth,
You'll remember from your predecessor Charles how
irritating the Commons can be. Let's work together on
this. You've got the keys, I've got the army - let's lock the
frightful devils out.
Non Regina,
Boris Rex

Aug 28, 2019

Dear Elizabeth,
Thanks for the suspension of parliament hoojamaflip. I'll hang on to the keys to the House tvm. If any of the old guard try to call on you at the Palace, tell them to sling their hook.
Best,
Boris Rex

In the UK, persons over the age of 75 were given free television licences by the BBC. Those in charge of the BBC were requesting more financial support at this time. In order to save money, the BBC was suggesting cancelling the free licences for the elderly, except those claiming benefits.

Aug 28, 2019

Dear BBC,
Will be aware of my warning to you re: why you MUST foot the bill for the over 75s. I am now asking you to ensure that all your news outlets accurately represent everything I say without framing it in critical or comical commentary.
De facto dictator,
Boris Rex

Aug 28, 2019

Dear Boris,
I hate people like...I was going to say which people I hate, but best to leave it as: I hate people. The numpty MPs will say a lot and do nothing. Most of the press are with us. We're nearly there.
Dom

Aug 31, 2019

Dear David,
We didn't think this through: a referendum may produce a result at variance with parliament's view. Which one represents the will of the people? On that cleft stick are we hoist...or stuck...or whatever.
Thesis in faeces,
Boris

Sep 3, 2019

Dear Boris,
Your pathetic party is full of snivelling worms. I heard Hammond on the BBC (Marxist-Leninist). He should be sectioned or beheaded. Do it. There's too much dead wood in the ranks. Lop it off. Remember what I said: eat or be eaten.
Dominic

Sep 3, 2019

Dear Dominic,
Slightly snaggy: seems the swines have spotted that you don't have a membo card. I know a guy in Belgravia who's got an engraving biz who could knock you up something dated 1996. Needs must. Eat this note.
Magnus avocado in solipsis,
Boris

Sep 3, 2019

Dear Dave,
Are you in the country or on hols? Was remembering a chat I had with old Boffo who told me that while you were in college you had a tendency to leave a silent sentinel in the bogs for Matron to flush. Was minded it

XIII

of it this week.
Solo excrementum in perpetua,
Boris

Sep 3, 2019

Dear Boris,
David is not doing letters, emails or phone calls at the
moment. He's got a frightfully huge autumn coming up
doing promos for his autobiog. and is taking a break-
ette before the storm. We're all well. Who are you
married to now?
Samantha

Sep 3, 2019

Dear Boris,
Did you catch me on telly? Hope so. I kept to Dominic's
script word for word so I hope you were pleased with it.
I'm also doing my best with the face thing: keeping it
cheery. Hope you spotted that. I didn't leak the wotsit
when I was doing Defence. Really.
Best,
Gavin

Sep 3, 2019

Dear Williamson,
Don't snivel. I had a fag at Eton whose job was to tie my
shoelaces and if I so much as reminded him that I like
double-bows, would burst into a stream of apologetic
mutterings. Awful creep. Remember, it's strength
through joy.
In domine non cluedo,
Boris

Sep 3, 2019

Dear Corbyn,
It is really quite extraordinary - nay unfathomable - as to why Labour would suggest that I would go back on my word about a date for a General Election. I would be most grateful if you and your gang of Nazi Trotskyists would withdraw this calumny.
Magnus Boris

On the 3rd September 2019, Dr Philip Lee, Conservative MP for Bracknell crossed the floor of the house to join the Liberal democrats, thereby losing the Conservative party their majority.

Sep 3, 2019

Dear Boris,
I don't want to sound in any way like some kind of superior head girl but from where I'm sitting (watching the tennis, actually), it rather does look as if you've lost your majority. Careless, or what? Whoops.
Best wishes,
Theresa

Sep 3, 2019

Dear Theresa,
Last time I was ticked off like that was when Matron found me smoking banana skins behind the Music block. I can tell you for nothing that I've brought turbocharged grit and steel to this whole Brexit matter, not your dog's brexit.
In domine dominic,
Boris

Dear Boris,
Stuff the traitor who's buggered off. I warned you before
that your shitty party is stuffed full of inferior genetic
material. Eva Peron didn't need crap like that.
Dominic

Sep 3, 2019

Dear Dominic,
Did I call a General Election or not? Could you clarify?
In myxamotosis exit,
Boris

Sep 3, 2019

Dear Nigel,
We need to meet. Can I suggest a rural locale to keep
the paps at bay? The delightful Duchess of Rutland has
made her lodge available.
In presto pesto,
Boris

Sep 3, 2019

Dear Lee O'Varadka,
You'll remember that Ireland used to be English. We
have proposed alternative arrangements to the
backstop in the form of wristbands as pioneered at
popular music festivals. I trust that traditional Irish
intransigence will not reject this.
Con funghi,
Boris

Oliver Letwin lost the whip on the 3rd September 2019, He had
brought a cross-party bill with Yvette Cooper (labour) known
as the 'Cooper-Letwin Act' that sought to extend the period
defined under Article 50 of the Treaty on European Union. It
was introduced to parliament on 3rd April 2019 and was finally
passed in August. It was repealed on the 23rd January 2020.

Sep 3, 2019

Dear Oliver,
Let me reassure you that there is of course no way that
Jacob accusing you of 'misunderstanding Parliament'
could be construed as being antisemitic.
Non judea in toto,
Boris

Sep 3, 2019

Dear Jacob,
When you sit down, could you text me with a translation
of 'legerdemain', which you just used in your speech?
Does it mean that it's going to be light tomorrow?
Da vinci codex,
Boris

Sep 3, 2019

Dear Dominic,
It's not looking good. I feel we're stuck between a rock
and a Cyclops. I've done everything you told me to, what
now?
In excelsis deo botox,
Boris

Sep 3, 2019

Dear Boris,
We're smashing the septic encrusted entitled elite and
putting in a new vibrant thrusting free open market-
loving go-getters like you and Rees-Mogg.
Nearly there,
Dominic

Sep 4, 2019

Dear Boris,
We're slashing and burning for christ's sake: lopping off
dead wood, deflating old farts, mowing down weeds,
destruction for construction.
Shape up for Christ's sake,
Dominic

Sep 5, 2019

Dear Boris,
I see you're using the phrase 'an insult to democracy'
about Corbyn's plans. Perhaps go easy on this or people
will look back at your insults and the words you use.
Apart from that, kill anyone in our way.
Dominic

**Joseph Johnson was Minister of State for Universities, Science
and Research and a member of his brother's cabinet. On the
5th September 2019 he resigned and stated he would not be
standing as an MP at the next election.**

Sep 5, 2019

Dear Boris,
We're cleaning out the stables: first the weebles
(remember: "weebles wobble but they don't fall down"
until you kick them.) and now your snivelling brother.
Give him a going over at the next family reunion.
Dominic

Sep 6, 2019

Dear Dominic,
I have a slight sense that your Grand Strategy is not
panning out exactly as you had outlined them. I feel

most unlike my hero Horatio on the bridge. Can you
reassure?
Amo amas amat,
Boris

Dear Boris,
Shape up ffs.
You are the Goliath who defeated David. Think how
masterful this 'chicken' narrative is. An election delayed
by a few days!!! Huge!!! Massive!!! And all the shock jocks
rooting for us even though we're maniacs! Think Trump.
Dominic

Dear Dominic,
Are we really, really, really going ahead with this
prorogation lark?
Minus maximus primus stove,
Boris

**Parliament was suspended between September 10 and 24.
Thus limiting the time for discussion regarding the terms and
conditions for leaving the European Union by members of parliament.**

Dear Dominic,
Times ahead: call a vote of no confidence in myself?
Break the law? Resign (even though I keep saying I'm
negotiating)? And it's all because your great plan has
foundered on the rock of bloody Corbyn not doing what
you said he would do.
Impasto in sanctus,
Boris

Sep 7, 2019

Dear Boris,
Be cool like the mountain stream, swift like the deer,
fierce like the eagle, courageous as the hedgehog. The
dead wood is falling away, and where it doesn't we're
burning it anyway. A phoenix will rise from the ashes
and crush the lily-livered beneath its hooves.
DC

Sep 7, 2019

Dear Boris,
Sorry missed meeting. Was in chats with Nigel. Think we
have a deal. Banks is onside with lashings of loot. It'll
make the weeds and wets (mostly women) completely
berserk. Let them rot or die in the flames.
We're nearly there.
Dominic

Sep 7, 2019

Dear Dominic,
Amber going is not a good look. I really think we should
have tried to keep her on board. She lent an air of
schoolmarmy respectability to our project. Don't tell
anyone: she reminded me of Matron.
Gaius Maximius russellus crouus,
Boris

Sep 7, 2019

Dear Boris,
Another one bites the dust: the more the better. Far
preferable they die outside the tent than in it. Let the
secret Commies like Ken Clarke and Rory Stewart
mourn while we burn her corpse. Why are people writing

in the papers that I'm mad?
Best,
Dominic

Amber Rudd resigned on the 7th September from the cabinet as Secretary of State for Work and Pensions. She stated she would not be standing for parliament at the next election.

Sep 8, 2019

Dear Boris,
We must control the narrative on Amber. We go on: she quit over Brexit, she's a remainer at heart etc. Keep away from anything to do with us forging this white hot steel-edged weapon slicing through the flabby tissue of old Tory sponges. Watch out: Nicky Morgan!
DC

Theresa May, in the spring of 2019 had appointed John Mann, a Labour MP, as an independent adviser to the government on antisemitism. She gave him the honour of a life peerage. He continued in his position as adviser in Boris Johnson's government.

Sep 8, 2019

Dear Boris,
Masterstroke pressing ahead with the May woman's appointment of John Mann as antisemitism tsar. You are of course our Tsar Tsar and as Cossacks we ride roughshod over the snivelling Tory waverers. One tip: Don't mention Travellers to Mann.
Best,
Dominic

Sep 8, 2019

Dear Dominic,
We have to get Bercow, take him behind the music block
and give him a beating. He reminds me of that too-
clever-by-half Sacha Baron Cohen. Get him out the
House, Dom.
In geranium et pelargonium,
Boris

Sep 8, 2019

Dear Boris,
Agreed. Is there a way we can get a new speaker in,
while parliament is prorogued? The MPs all come back
and Rees-Mogg is sitting there instead!!! Ha bloody ha!
Dominic

Sep 9, 2019

Dear Dominic,
How do you think I'm going down in Dublin? They're
nice, kind, simple folk and I get the impression that they
think I'm quite a guy. This border thing is going to be a
walk in the park, I reckon.
In scrotum credo,
Boris

Sep 9, 2019

Dear Boris,
Ireland's a waste of space. Don't worry about it. Same
goes for the House of Commons. Great that we've got
that dump out the way. Get out of the place asap so I
can tell you what we're doing next. Their so-called 'law'
(hah!) is just a bit of crap we can flush away.
Dominic

Dear Dominic,
To be absolutely honest with you, Dom, I'm getting worried about our numbers. I know we've got bloody fine people with us like John Mann and Kate Hoey but I'm really not sure how our ship is going to get to port.
Pneumonia non pythagoras,
Boris

Dear Dominic,
I can feel it in my bones that we're losing Nicky Morgan. I've never been a great fan but she's got a certain kind of womanly charm about her. I fear it won't look good in the press if she walks out.
In desperandum non carborundum,
Boris

Dear Boris,
Nicky who? Who cares? Who are these useless fly-by-nights? How many solid English Brexit-voters have any idea who she is, what she stands for or whether she's worth spending more than a second or two of the hypocritical rubbish that you will say about her? 2 at most.
D

Dear Boris,
What did I say? Hold the nerve: and the weak fall away. Now the insufferable Berkowski is stepping aside!!! Die, Berk, die! Find some bit of pap to fill the seat.
Triumph awaits,
Dominic

Sep 9, 2019

Dear Dominic,
I've cracked the backstop probby!!! How about this? We
tell each and every cow, bullock, chicken, duck, potato,
and loaf of bread, it can - if it chooses - to be Unionist or
Irish? What do you think?
Cumulus nimbus,
Boris

Sep 9, 2019

Dear Boris,
The losers in that House of Commons of yours might
think they can get open access to our messages about
Brexit but you can tell them I've just chucked my phone
in the Thames.
Dominic

Sep 9, 2019

Dear Dominic,
I've put your idea to people that everything on the island
of Ireland goes on as before after we've left the EU bit
people say that it doesn't really do it for the Unionists
who like us and them to be in the same country.
Etna et Vesuvius non jocula,
Boris

Sep 9, 2019

Dear Boris,
I love the look of that Ian Austin guy. Espesh the way he
uses any excuse to fire off at Corbyn. He's going to lose
his seat. Will you fix him some crap job with us? Saudi
Arabia Link man? Holocaust Tsar?
Dominic

Sep 10, 2019

Dear Dominic,
Looking at Theresa's honours list is a pretty good guide
for you as to what I've got up my sleeve for you, old
chap. Delete this from your phone. The rabble have
passed some prying bill and will do what they can to
throw mud at us.
Victor podium larynx,
Boris

**Three judges at The High Court in Scotland ruled that Boris
Johnson's prorogation of Parliament was unlawful. They said
unanimously that Johnson's suspension of Parliament was
unlawful "because it had the purpose of stymying parliament".**

Sep 11, 2019

Dear Dominic,
Have you seen that some court in Scotland has said that
our prorogation is unlawful. We may need to put out
some emollient words asap.
Sub judice in radio,
Boris

Sep 11, 2019

Dear Boris,
We've been through this ffs. The long game is going to
mean shoving Scotland into the hands of the Euro
Hitlers. We're not going to let some jumped-up
Scottish judge tell us what to do. Eat them.
Dominic

Sep 11, 2019

Dear Dominic,
I'm not so sure about this. Technically speaking the people up there are at the moment part of the UK which means that - I think I've got this right - the House of Commons does partially belong to them. They are included, if you get me.
Hibernia post mortem,
Boris

Sep 11, 2019

Dear Boris,
As ever, you're not concentrating. They play bagpipes. Need I say more? In the meantime, I've got my team burning out the databases on every computer between Trafalgar Square and Millbank. Have you told me the names of every single one of your companions?
Dominic

Sep 11, 2019

Dear Dominic,
This blooming Scots thing is not going away. They're saying that even though they're thousands of miles away in the Orkneys, they can tell us what we do in our parliament. Get your thinking hat on, we need to get out of this one quick.
Caveat pronto toto,
Boris

Dominic Grieve was MP for Beaconsfield from 1997 to September 2019. He had been appointed Attorney General by Michael Howard but lost the post under David Cameron. In September 2019 he lost the whip for voting to block a no-deal Brexit.

Sep 11, 2019

Dear Dominic,
I can't remember what we told the Queen. I heard the god-forsaken Grieve's self-righteous blooming whine on the radio earlier. Do we have anything on him? Personal life? Well, OK, maybe not that one - anything else?
Non in flagrante toga,
Boris

Sep 11, 2019

Dear Boris,
You're right about one thing at least, for a change - as you're usually wrong about everything. Yes, Grieve is Public Enemy No 1. We have to destroy him and crush him till his body stops twitching. Do you know the Duke of E.? We may need him to put the squeeze on HRH.
DC

Sep 11, 2019

Dear Boris,
Were you - or anyone you know - at Eton or Oxford with any of the Supreme Court judges? We need dark stuff on any of them and get it to what's-his-face at the Mail. Your line in public - don't laugh - is Toffs in Wigs versus The People. Get on with it.
Dominic

Sep 11, 2019

Dear Dominic,
Not sure I can carry on much longer with Andrea L. She
was on the BBC saying that we can't release
Yellowhammer because it will put the shits up the
public. Not her words but you get the drift. Do you think
Angela's for the shredder?
O tempore finis,
Boris

Sep 11, 2019

Dear Boris,
Leadsom's loyal. Anyway, now that Amber's gone, we
need Leadsom out there to keep up our fluff count.
There'll come a moment when quite a few of them will
have to be culled, but not yet.
Dominic

Sep 11, 2019

Dear Dominic,
You know the line we're feeding the baying hordes that
we suspended Parliament because we're too darned
well busy to keep it open? I've just remembered I texted
Dad telling him that we were doing it to stop the traitors
debagging us. Problem?
In hoc pater,
Boris

Sep 11, 2019

Dear Boris,
Problem??????!!!!!!! Courier me the phone right now!
Dominic

Sep 11, 2019

Dear Dominic,
I'm afraid that particular course of action is not exactly
possible in the full meaning of the word. Since that time,
I have been in a variety of establishments and - I know
this was inept of me - I fear it is no longer about my
person.
Connubio nihil cogito,
Boris

**Arlene Foster was First Minister of Northern Ireland and Leader
of the DUP from 2015 - 2021.**

Sep 11, 2019

Dear Arlene,
In the event of the British government being able to
provide Northern Ireland with an unlimited supply of
Union Jacks, to what extent would you and your
esteemed colleagues be happy for Belfast airport to be
run by the Irish government?
Quis possiblo facit est,
Boris

Sep 11, 2019

Dear Dominic,
Holy Holofernes, have you seen the headline in the
Mirror? Says I lied to the Queen. Bloody bad opioids.
That's not the word is it? Optics. Yes. I thought you were
going to make sure I don't look like a blooming beached
whale.
Bacteria in cranium,
Boris

xxx

Sep 12, 2019

Dear Boris,
On the hour, every hour, get yourself in front of a mirror, in private and say to your image in the mirror: 'I did not lie to the Queen. I did not lie to the Queen' over and over and over until you've convinced yourself.
Dominic

Sep 12, 2019

Dear Boris,
The pebble falls into the river, there is no mark for people to see when they walk past next day.
Dominic

Sep 13, 2019

Dear Dominic,
I'm looking into whether we can build a tunnel between Northern Ireland and Scotland in time for October 31st. I've been talking to some engineering chappies and I'm pretty sure this could be the solution.
Sub terra sub superba,
Boris

Sep 13, 2019

Dear Dominic,
Feels like a superb Saturday. I've been on radio telling porkies about what I did or didn't say. Oily Cam's book comes out vomming all over me - and this is the point - and none of it harms me. Truth is so yesterday.
Veritas hocus pocus,
Boris

Dear Dominic,
Any chance you can stop sending me to all these
blooming places where people shout at me? What about
places like Sevenoaks?
Suburbia superba,
Boris

Dear Boris,
I told you before that Morgan has to be wasted. I'm right
about everything. Just do it. She's not worth the breath
she breathes. Don't talk to me till you've done it.
Dominic

Dear Boris,
Got one of your crusty Oxford chums on to something:
in 1294 the Sheriff-Lieutenant of the Duchy of
Huntingdon was allowed to overrule a statute on
account of the Black Death. We're in the clear! It'll get No
Deal through!
Dominic

Dear Dominic,
Blooming heck: this is gold dust. I told you the old
Oxford connections would come in handy. Do you think
we're going to lose any more MPs? It's not a great look.
Rubric hubris alitalia,
Boris

Sep 15, 2019

Dear Boris,
Remember that the last few weeks in parliament have had zero effect on millions of voters. It's too complicated to bother with and comes over as unfair ways of stopping them having what they want. Just keep on saying you're giving them what they want. Job done.
DC

Sep 15, 2019

Dear Dominic,
Some of the polls are looking good. I guess it's because I sound like I am really going to deliver. It doesn't matter what I'm going to deliver, so long as I deliver. Which leads me to another point: what if I don't deliver?
Post hoc post hic,
Boris

Sep 16, 2019

Dear Boris,
And I know it's a tough call because you're such an unreliable slob, but you are the colossus fighting the nerds and nasties in parliament and the courts, to deliver this bold, clean, pure thing: Brexit. We're nearly there.
Dominic

Sep 16, 2019

Dear Dominic,
I'm really getting it. It's not about the truth or facts is it? It never was. It's about a story - island race, GREAT Britain, standing alone, sod off jonny foreigner, we won't be bossed about. And I can deny I said what I said, so

what!
Fantasia veritas est,
Boris

Sep 16, 2019

Dear Dominic,
I'm finding the schedule a bit wearing. Any chance I
could call a pause and take an away-break in my
favourite watering-hole in Somerset? I thought your plan
was to twiddle our thumbs till Hallowe'en and then drive
us out of Europe in a Roller.
Transit gloria,
Boris

Sep 16, 2019

Dear Dominic,
Where is Luxembourg? I got out the plane somewhere
between Moscow and Dublin and they told me I was in
Luxembourg. Hardly anyone lives in the place so I've no
idea why you sent me there. Sad to say, the whole
population turned out to boo me.
Audio ad nauseam,
Boris

Sep 16, 2019

Dear Boris,
Your Luxembourg debacle doesn't matter in the
slightest. It may make the media cackle but in the Dog
and Gun, I can assure you, you are top Trumps, doing
what the people asked you to do, with only a bunch of
corrupt crooks in parliament trying to stop it happening.
DC

Dear Dominic,
Did you follow what was going on at the Supreme wotsit today? I watched about five minutes of it and woke up 2 hours later.
Somnolens ambulare,
Boris

Dear Boris,
Whatever the Supreme Court says doesn't matter. Our hardcore support doesn't care. It's just another trick by the elite to cheat them of the Referendum. Go back to sleep.
Dominic

Dear Dominic,
We have the terrifying prospect that Corbyn's Brexit proposal is reasonable. You need to get your skates on and find a way of proving that it's all a trap to lure us into the jaws of Putin. Or China. Or Iran. Or all three.
Chianti non gratis,
Boris

Dear Dominic,
Fear I've become a trifle muddled over whether we're negotiating with the EU, not negotiating, pretending to negotiate, or pretending not to negotiate. Can you clarify asap?
Romeo bravo,
Boris

The Conservatives had set up an investigation into islamaphobia in parliament. It was led by Swaran Singh. Baroness Sayeeda Warsi, a former Conservative party Chairman, now sitting in the House of Lords was keen to see results. When Boris Johnson worked for the Spectator, he had written an article criticising the wearing of Burkas by Muslim women saying it made them look like letterboxes. Many people criticised his comments.

Sep 20, 2019

Dear Dominic,
You seen the fuss about so-called 'Islamophobia' in the Conservative Party? Tricky one to handle because Warsi is on to the fact that we can't come up with a definition. Obvs we can't! Any definition is bound to net me and my letterbox gag.
Onus in pandemonium,
Boris

Sep 20, 2019

Dear Boris,
You need a bit of anti-muslim stuff beating away at the heart of the Tories to keep your base spiced up. If you start mouthing a load of PC muck you're going to lose votes to Farage.
Dominic

The Sunday Times ran an article about Boris Johnson's friendship with the glamourous American business woman, Jennifer Arcuri. There was comment that she had had access to three overseas trade deals and possibly public money.

Sep 22, 2019

Dear Dominic,
There's an outrageous story about me in the Sunday Times with a picture of me with someone who is no longer my companion and suggesting I manipulated funds. They'll be digging up the Eton tuck shop scandal next. Stop them doing this.
In loco parenthesis,
Boris

Sep 22, 2019

Dear Boris,
I can hold the fort on your little pump prime scandal, but the Eton Tuck Shop issue might go viral. I need dates, times, figures. What was the stuff? Orange and Black? After Eights? Bentincks? Petits Fours? Bath Olivers? Details please. Urgent.
Dominic

Sep 23, 2019

Dear Dominic,
You need to put some big-hitters out there to defend my handling of Jennifer Arcuri's company. You must make clear that what I do with public money is my business.
Pro patria tori,
Boris

Sep 23, 2019

Dear Boris,
You seem to have forgotten: we've chucked out all the big-hitters. You'll have to bumble your way through this one on your own. In the meantime I've found a statute

from 1268 which will enable is to abolish the Supreme Court.
Dominic

Dear Jacob,
Technically speaking you'll know that in actual fact it wasn't me in person who actually went to see the Queen. You'll remember that technically speaking in actual fact it was in fact you.
Non mea culpa,
Boris

Dear Dominic,
Sticky probby: the Supreme thingy ruling isn't good news is it? Reminds me of time the Bullingdon was up before the Proctors for smashing the college windows. We slimed out of it! Should work again.
Anus miraculus,
Boris

The Supreme Court Judgement was given on the 24th September. It found that the prorogation of parliament was unlawful because it had been made with the purpose of stymying parliament.

Dear Boris,
Screw them. Who are they? A bunch of toffs who've read a few books. Ignore them. What can they do about it? They haven't got an army. Do your thing at the UN. You'll be a smash.
Dominic

Sep 24, 2019

Dear Matron,
Do you remember that time my hamper from Mummy
didn't arrive and I was burst sad and you gave me some
lovely choccy eclairs? Well I'm in a spot of diff at the mo,
could you send me something delish?
Compulsio per femina,
Boris

Sep 24, 2019

Dear Dominic,
I'm in the lavatory.
Cloaca problematica,
Boris

Sep 24, 2019

Dear Nanny,
Seems like we've got to go back to the House. Not sure
why. Look, I'm in the US at the moment and haven't
packed a spare pair of trousers. Do you think you could
chuck a suitcase together for me and courier it round to
Number 10?
Toga non in casa,
Boris

Sep 24, 2019

Dear Borry,
I stopped working for your family 35 years ago. I fear
you've got muddled. Are you alright? If it's any help, why
not order a pair of trousers online and get them sent
round to Number 10. Is your father still as frisky as he
always was?
Love Nanny

Michel Barnier, a Frenchman, was the EU official negotiating the terms of the UK's withdrawal. He met with Boris Johnson several times during the autumn of 2019.

Sep 24, 2019

Dear Barnier,
Bonjour! Un probleme! Les juges declare que je suis illegal! Impossible! Je suis Boris! C'est possible que Je can't quitte Angleterre!!! Vous etes oblige de retourner here to continuer le negotiations merde.
De facto galactico,
Boris

Sep 25, 2019

Dear Dominic,
Did you see my blusterfest in the Commons today? I am good, damned good. The way I was thrashing them, no one would ever have guessed that it was me and Moggy who got nabboed.
In excelsis ego,
Boris

Donald Trump, then President of the United States was hoping that the Ukraine President would provide evidence of wrong-doing by Hunter Biden, thus helping to discredit Joe Biden whose bid to take the presidency in 2020 was already under way.

Sep 26, 2019

Dear Donald,
I've read your convo with Pres of Ukraine. I admire your style. The biz of heavying him with 'I would like you to do us a favour' has got me thinking about trying it out on the DUP. Like you, I can withhold some dosh to give it teeth.
Hocus pocus in flagrante,
Boris

Dear Boris,
Well done for last night. Everyone's talking this morning about 'language' and no one's talking about the Supreme Court judgement. Result! You need some more distractors in your bag: something on race and crime usually works.
Dominic

Dear Dominic,
I confess I'm a trifle confused: there's a law saying that I've got to go and grovel to the Brussels sprouts and ask for an extension, but you've scripted me to keep saying we leave on Oct 31, deal or no deal. Am I missing something?
Ego blotto in vitro,
Boris

Dear Nigel,
We need to talk: alleyway, back of Number 10. Hop over the wall and I'll meet you by the third oak tree. I think I've wangled a Theresa-plus deal but you've got to pretend it gives us sovereignty or I'm buggered. I'll bring the whisky.
Nonplus minus maximus,
Boris

Dear Boris,
Great guy. Beautiful guy - that's me. I've discovered that my private letters are not private. NOT PRIVATE!!! The

Democrat Clinton Obama witch-hunt have broken
through my firewall. So this is my LAST LETTER!!! Burn
your boxers. Keep safe.
God bless America,
Donald

Sep 26, 2019

Dear Sayeeda,
Thank you so much for your sincere and incisive letters.
I am delighted to inform you, young lady, we have dealt
with all matters pertaining to Islamophobia and the
matter is now closed.
In addendum appendix,
Boris

Sep 27, 2019

Dear Dominic,
I've put all my ministers on top alert to explain clearly to
interviewers that we will obey the law by disobeying it.
Cranium torpor,
Boris

Sep 27, 2019

Dear Dominic,
Loved your quip how compared with the Referendum,
leaving the EU on Oct 31 will be a 'walk in the park'.
Don't tell anyone, but I went for a walk in the park
yesterday and trod in some dog doo.
Terra faeces,
Boris

Sep 28, 2019

Dear Dominic,
Now I've got PC Plod crawling all over my accounts.
When I was mayor it was my job to splash the cash and
some close friends got lucky.
Pro bono,
Boris

Sep 29, 2019

Dear Dominic,
I'm doing what you said: I'm denying everything.
Everything they throw at me I'm just saying it's rubbish.
Enjoying it.
Dramatis personae exit,
Boris

Sep 30, 2019

Dear Dominic,
Loving strategy of sending out all my troops to say they
trust me. Ho Ho! I don't even trust myself. By the way
have you seen my trousers?
Credo et fido,
Boris

Oct 1, 2019

Dear Dominic,
I think I've cracked it! Did you ever read the wonderful
book, 'The Invisible Man' by H.G.Wells? I think it's a clear
way forward for Ireland. I have in mind that invisible men
could be customs posts. What do you think?
Quis quid quo quad quim,
Boris

Oct 1, 2019

Dear Nicky Morgan,
Superb on Newsnight! I owe you a huge debt of
gratitude for your loyalty. The fact that you have
reversed all your previous beliefs is a great feat of
political judgement. Dominic wondered if you could look
a little less 'scared rabbit'?
Opium sanctus est,
Boris

Oct 3, 2019

Dear Dominic,
I gather some people in Northern Ireland think they live
in some kind of single entity they call Ireland. Have you
heard of this? Presumably not many of them think along
these lines?
Animus maximus,
Boris

Oct 3, 2019

Dear Dominic,
Got a slight verbal dilemma to overcome. When I was
asked if I'd seek an extension I did say I would rather die
in a ditch. The news has broken saying that in actual
fact I would seek an extension. Advice?
Post mortem in situ,
Boris

Oct 4, 2019

Dear Boris,
Not to worry, just attack Corbyn, it worked well in your
speech when you could promise nothing about
immigration.
As ever,
Dominic

Oct 5, 2019

Dear Dominic,
Your slogan 'Get Brexit Done' has been a winner. All credit to you. However - and please don't take this as criticism - I have had a thought about it in the cold light of day: what if, for example, we don't get Brexit done?
Crocus pocus in arcadia vixit,
Boris

Oct 5, 2019

Dear Dominic,
The term 'customs posts' is proving to be a bit sticky for the less co-operative people in Ireland. Can we put in thinking time on what else they might be called thereby neutralising their need to complain? 'Orange Points'? 'Border Bollards'?
Fantasia maior,
Boris

Oct 6, 2019

Dear Dominic,
What about locking myself in Number 10 on October 31st? Then the police could come and arrest me. I would then be a martyred hero, sacrificed on the altar of fulfilling the will of the people.
Sapiens acqua san pellegrino,
Boris

Oct 7, 2019

Dear Dominic,
I don't think you're doing enough to back me up on the JA affair. Well, let's not call it an affair! JA case. I need you to say something unequivocal and faintly

threatening. And you may need to get a shredder down to County Hall tonight.
Pubis jocularis,
Boris

Oct 7, 2019

Dear Dominic,
The EU Nazis have rejected our proposals. Is this good or bad? (I haven't always given your Machiavellian plans the attention they deserve.) Presumably we'll be able to blame Barnier when the EU puts up Stalag Luft watchtowers?
Impunitas pasta,
Boris

Oct 8, 2019

Dear Dominic,
I think I've cracked it. I nip over to Dublin again and tell Leo wotsit that he's got to leave the EU. Not deffo sure there's time to fix this before Oct 31 but fingers and toes crossed.
Tempus fugit panto fixit,
Boris

Oct 8, 2019

Dear Dominic,
How ok are you that the media are talking about what's happening as 'What Cummings wants'? I'm a tad concerned that it looks as if we elected chappies are being run by someone who wasn't.
Intellectum rectum,
Boris

Dear Dominic,
I've mislaid my Dictionary of Insults. Have you borrowed it? I need it for some choice words to cover this climate rabble. When I was their age I was working off steam in a rugger scrum.
Plebs scrotum,
Boris

Dear Dominic,
Am reading accounts saying that when we crash out of the EU there will be shortages. Wow! Are you stocking up on any stuff? I've slipped a couple of crates of Chateauneuf du Pape in the boot of my car and a hundred white shirts. How about you?
Vino inebrio,
Boris

Dear Dominic,
We need to make contingency arrangements for that ditch I said i'd rather die in. It's probable that it's my only option left so to avoid my demise, would you fill it in?
Fossa comicus non est,
Boris

Dear Dominic,
The whole point is Jennifer Arcurri was an expert. People just don't appreciate how expert she was.
Epidermis impervius,
Boris

Oct 9, 2019

Dear Dominic,
I got a damned rude letter from Khan's lot saying that my letter "doesn't answer any of the questions we asked". I've written back to them saying, 'Well, don't bloody ask the questions, then!'
Detestatio omnia vincit,
Boris

A meeting was set up at Thornton Manor near Liverpool between Leo Varadkar, the Irish Prime Minister and Boris Johnson to discuss the difficulties regarding a border on the island of Ireland. Eire in south of the island would be in the EU and Northern Ireland, as part of the UK, would not be in the EU when Brexit was finalised.

When writing for the Spectator, Boris Johnson had suggested disparagingly that Liverpudlians were 'hooked on grief'.

Oct 9, 2019

Dear Dominic,
Are you sending me to Liverpool to meet Leo wotsit? Do you know they've exaggerated some little quip I made about Liverpuddlians ? Perhaps I'd better go in disguise?
Incognito pomegranato,
Boris

Oct 11, 2019

Dear Dominic,
I'm afraid I lost my briefing notes just before my chat with Leo wotsit. I told him we're fine with something he kept calling an 'all-Ireland' something. Is that ok with you? What about Arlene and Jacob?
Toyota placenta previa,
Boris

Oct 12, 2019

Dear Dominic,
My Uxbridge constituency is looking flaky: polls suggest
it's gone remoan. Thanks for parachuting me into
Beaconsfield today. I could kick out Dominic Grievous
Bodily Harm there perhaps.
Conundrum colon,
Boris

Oct 12, 2019

Dear Dominic,
If these Irish people don't like your plans, I have an
alternative up my sleeve: why don't we suggest they
emigrate?
Inspiratio transit exfoliant,
Boris

Oct 12, 2019

Dear Dominic,
I woke up this morning with another idea: everyone in
Northern Ireland can sign up for the UK Customs Union
or the EU Customs Union or both! Then each person
chooses which of the two kinds of imports and exports
they sign up to too.
Multiplicationis pollux,
Boris

Oct 13, 2019

Dear Dominic,
Thinking ahead: there is a slight probby of some people
being a bit poor et cetera. What we need to do is find
ways to tuck it out of the way. Can you give me a ten-
point plan on how to make poverty not look bad?

Bonus alibi bonus bonus,
Boris

Oct 14, 2019

Dear Dominic,
I think you're dead right to have gone all out for law and
order. The key thing here is for us to not let anyone
frame this with our record on police cuts. We can learn a
thing or two from Donald on the idea that crime is
foreign.
Find our Mexicans!
Con funghi,
Boris

Oct 15, 2019

Dear Dominic,
How come these unionists and loyalists are so darned
keen on being attached to us? When did this malarkey
start? We didn't cover this stuff on my classics course.
Antebellum vellum,
Boris

**Theresa May had given money to Northern Ireland at the start
of her Brexit negotiations. It looked like a bribe to get them to
vote with the Conservatives on her Brexit bills.**

Oct 16, 2019

Dear Dominic,
Tell the DUP they can have Donegal. Or Glasgow. Or
Wales.
Pro bono non Bono,
Boris

Oct 16, 2019

Dear Dominic,
Have you checked the magic money tree to see whether
it's got any more billions to cram into Arlene's mouth?
Ad maxima per asparagus,
Boris

Oct 16, 2019

Dear Dominic,
Looks like I've got to do what that wretched son of a
Communist, Benn is making me do. Bloody annoying
I've got the 'die in a ditch ' thing hanging over me. Can
we make out it was in jest?
In limbo ad nauseam,
Boris

**It had been agreed that if MPS had not approved a Brexit deal
or voted for a no-deal Brexit, by the 19th October, 2019, the
government must request an extension to Article 50 to January
31st 2020.**

Oct 17, 2019

Dear Dominic,
You were a genius to have switched horses. For
decades we've poked Paddy in the eye and backed the
Orangemen. You're so right. All we had to do is switch
over: dump the DUP.
Caesar saladus,
Boris

Oct 18, 2019

Dear Dominic,
Pretty certain we'll win the vote on Saturday. The Labour MPs in Leave seats are going to do it for us. Fine people. Looking forwards to seeing your plans later on how we shaft them in the General Election.
Victor ludorum ego,
Boris

Oct 18, 2019

Dear Dominic,
Thanks to you I'm having to pump out gallons of bs about 'workers' rights' in the hope of netting one more Labour bonehead. I find it difficult to say the word 'worker' let alone glue it to the word 'rights'. Needs must. Dammit.
Excrementus consumato,
Boris

Oct 19, 2019

Dear Dominic,
Blooming heck who does this Letwin oik think he is? No one can make me write a letter. Does he think he's my Housemaster?
Fungus prospectus,
Boris

Oct 19, 2019

Dear Dominic,
Ha ha ha. Up their noses. Did I show them? Yes I did. Like the time Head of House made me apologise to a fag for snaffling his jam but I bribed him to withdraw his complaint. I got it done.
Pro mobo non tibia,
Boris

Oct 19, 2019

Dear Dominic,
Why don't I secretly gather Moggy, Govey and Hancocky together in the House today while no one else is there and we just leave the EU? Then the mob come back in Monday morning and ha ha ha we've done it!!! What a wheeze!
In absentia pocus hocus,
Boris

Oct 21, 2019

Dear Dominic,
O hell's bells. Seems like the damnable Euro-nobs are saying they would be willing to grant an extension. So much for their effusive words to me last week. You just can't take them at their word. Where has trust in politics gone?
Pan mortadella in fossa est,
Boris

Oct 21, 2019

Dear Dominic,
Do I have to spend another day in the sweaty HoC today? I've just discovered a splendid little gourmet pub in Oxfordshire and I was rather hoping to take the squeeze out and give it a whirl. What do you think?
Patum pepperum non capsicum forte,
Boris

Oct 22, 2019

Dear Dominic,
Where are you? Various odd-bods and cranks are going through the deal finding things they don't like. They're

like that pathetic worm, Bradbrooke Minor, who used to pick the onions out of his spag bol at Eton.
Ignosce illis, non enim sciunt quod faciunt,
Boris

Dear Dominic,
Was just dozing off when I thought I heard someone playing bagpipes. Reminded me I need clarification on Scotland: is it actually a country or a very large county? And what do they actually do up there?
Hibernia inferno Hadrian cognoscit,
Boris

Dear Dominic,
You really have to get on and decide if we are having a General Election or not. I've had dear Laura on my press mobile telling me to make up my mind as if it's my mind that has to be made up.
Hurry up please.
Velociraptor fugit,
Boris

Dear Dominic,
Can I clarify: when the evil Corb asks me questions about clauses and numbers and facts, I really don't have to answer, do I? Just talk about the IRA, right?
Platitudo tournedos,
Boris

Oct 24, 2019

Dear Dominic,
Got into serious probs with the squeeze. I was half
asleep; squeeze was making scrambled egg and was
taking an age and I blurted out - a tad irritatedly - 'Get
breakfast done!' I'm in trouble. Could you send her some
roses? In my name of course.
In canis casa,
Boris

Oct 24, 2019

Dear Dominic,
Do I know all the people in No10? I'm watching briefings
from the inestimable Laura and others from windmill
Peston and I've no idea who they're from nor how they
tally with each other. Are there any bods in the cupboard
under the stairs?
Occludo pommodoro,
Boris

Oct 24, 2019

Dear Dominic,
I'm not 100% sure that I'm up to speed on all this. Can
you confirm several things: has the Bill passed or not?
Are there checks between Northern Ireland and the rest
of the UK? Am I wearing my trousers? Respond asap.
Pronto tonto in video est,
Boris

Oct 27, 2019

Dear Dominic,
Did you see the Mail's pic of Corbyn napping while the
All Blacks game was on? Terrific. Keeps the traitor

theme going. Luckily, no paps were anywhere near me at the time, so that's a try and conversion to me. All's fair in love and war.
Anglia non Angela,
Boris

Oct 29, 2019

Dear Dominic,
What's our big thing today? It's not Brexit anymore is it? Apols: late night last night. Trying to finish a book about how Caligula has had a bad press. Election! Is that today's big thing?
Carpe diem et tutti frutti,
Boris

Oct 31, 2019

Dear Dominic,
Are you still absolutely sure that enabling the departure of Ken, Nicky, Philip, Amber, Justin et al is the right ticket? I fear we might lose Surbiton Woman.
Domine dominic domino marguerita,
Boris

Oct 31, 2019

Dear Dominic,
When we form the next government can we look at putting through some legislation to abolish October 31? I fear that it may become some kind of satirical anniversary which would undermine my prestige and gravitas.
Pestilentia in paella,
Boris

Nov 1, 2019

Dear Dominic,
Tremendous that Donald weighed in for us yesterday.
Thanks for setting that up. Can we prevail upon him to
make further interventions e.g. on our policies on
expanding grammar schools, on our tough policy on
Disability Benefit etc?
Quid pro quo status quo,
Boris

Nov 2, 2019

Dear Dominic,
Damned annoying England crumbled. I was rather
hoping to grab some glory off the back of a victory:
standing with the men, rugger ball under my arm,
showing up Corbyn as a sissy Arsenal fan.
Non victor linoleum est,
Boris

Nov 3, 2019

Dear Dominic,
There really is a limit to the number of times I'm
prepared to take my jacket off and walk round smelly
hospitals and schools pretending to care. Let's have a
bit of hope: show me opening a good restaurant in
Buckinghamshire.
Excessatio in panettone,
Boris

Nov 4, 2019

Dear Dominic,
What was your stay in Russia all about then? Have you
got special interests I don't know about? Vodka?

Dachas? Tolstoy? Lenin?
Ma fia con brio,
Boris

Nov 6, 2019

Dear Dominic,
I detect a little faltering at the tiller. Yesterday was not
the best of times. A bit of slippage. And for once, not my
fault. Is Gove powdering his nose again?
Modus implodus,
Boris

Nov 6, 2019

Dear Dominic,
I'm not sure your latest slogan 'You know you can trust
the Tories' is a good one. I fear it might give the more
forensic members of Fleet Street an excuse to probe
where we'd rather they didn't.
Preferens costa brava,
Boris

Nov 8, 2019

Dear Dominic,
Loving the discredit-Corbyn agenda. Note of caution for
you: watch out for a possible bounce back to us. In
which case, we must keep media away from our more
'patriotic' followers.
Camera obscura triceps,
Boris

Nov 9, 2019

Dear Dominic,
One overfilled glass and a blurring of finicky details over
Northern Ireland and questions are being asked as to
whether I know what I'm doing. I put it to you: do I know
what I'm doing? I ask myself: do I know what I'm doing?
Tosca Nintendo,
Boris

Nov 10, 2019

Dear Dominic,
A gem of good news: the investigation into my grant to
the queen of technology and pole dancing has been
suspended. I am untouchable. I am Boris.
Ego lamborghini,
Boris

Nov 10, 2019

Dear Dominic,
Could you keep the snoopers away from my Russian
amigos? There's a splash about them in the Sunday
Times. Don't break any legs but a little leaning can be a
dangerous thing (wink wink).
Pro umbrella sub pelvis,
Boris

Nov 11, 2019

Dear Dominic,
Sozz about my trampesque show at Senotaph:
aftermath of a bender with the old Bullingdon boys.
Superb remodelling of the footage - congrats. How did
you wangle that? Did they pick up on the angle of
Corbyn's bowing?

Pro patria tori,
Boris

Dear Dominic,
Election going swimmingly. I think. Tad worried we
might be treading water in some areas. Ah - perhaps an
unwise metaphor to use in present circumstances in all
places north of Watford. Can we keep Gove off the
screens? And off something else?
Acqua in machina,
Boris

Dear Dominic,
I'm all for sticking to the fine old Tory tradition of calling
anything or anyone that isn't Tory, 'barmy', 'crackpot' or
'bonkers'. I remember dear old Hailsham saying as
much. Just a tad bothered it could rebound. Do we have
all our marbles?
Tango in pesto,
Boris

Dear Dominic,
I'm sick of you putting me into state schools and NHS
hospitals and getting me to sing songs I don't know and
shake hands with people I don't want to meet. Anyway,
what do the wheels on the bus do? Why aren't they
singing about Julia Caesar?
Omnibus in transit,
Boris

Nov 15, 2019

Dear Boris,
The word 'communism' with a small 'c' involves the ownership and control of the means of production being in the hands of the working class. The state running a service is...er...just the state running a service e.g. like the police.
Hope this helps,
Michael Rosen

Nov 15, 2019

Dear Boris,
Further to my previous correspondence with you about communism: can you clear up whether you think the BBC is as 'communist' in structure and ownership as Labour's broadband proposals, more 'communist' or less 'communist'?
Michael Rosen

Nov 16, 2019

Dear Dominic,
Please give me a fact check first thing every morning eg where is Darlington? What is communism? How many children have I got? Etc etc.
Octopus maximus dulce vita,
Boris

Nov 16, 2019

Dear Boris,
You keep popping up in schools and hospitals. You seem to make sure that they aren't private ones. Isn't it your theory that the schools and the health service are a bit communist?
Michael Rosen

Nov 16, 2019

Dear Dominic,
Love Moggy to bits but do you think perchance there's a
whiff of the dodgy about him? - 'illuminati' gag at poor
old Ollie Letwin, retweeting that German AfD stuff, going
on about Soros, hanging out with the Traditional Britain
Group (gasp!)?
Rictus rectum,
Boris

Nov 17, 2019

Dear Dominic,
O for God's sake, the Azurri woman has turned up again.
She's going to be all over ITV tonight whingeing on and
on. Can't we find a distractor? How about we revive the
Blunkett thing again? Needs must, Dom. Get on with it.
Capuchino in flagrante,
Boris

Nov 18, 2019

Dear Dominic,
I'm finding it pretty damned hard to talk up the idea that
we're going to do all these marvellous things if people
keep banging on at me about why haven't we done them
before.
Mucus in cranium,
Boris

Nov 18, 2019

Dear Dominic,
Did you see the CBI stuff: Corbyn got slammed with the antisemitism thing! Excellent. Mind you, couldn't help thinking it must have been either luck or good management that a Muslim businessman didn't whack me over the head with Islamophobia, eh?
Bravo amigos,
Boris

Nov 21, 2019

Dear Dominic,
That's great you pulled me out of the head to head on Channel 4 Sunday. Maybe I'm not at my best faced with a little oik like Corbyn. Luckily I had the media claiming I wasn't a total disaster! Where next? A pub in Mayfair?
Hero in hummus,
Boris

Nov 21, 2019

Dear Chrishnan Guru-Martha,
Sozz I can't make the Sunday debate with Corbyn, I've got an evening in with the vintage slosh, turning the bottles.
In absentia pro linguini,
Boris

Nov 25, 2019

Dear Dominic,
We're really got to get the media off the truth wagon. They keep banging on and on at me about truth, truth, truth. We need a new slogan. How about, 'Truth is a complex matter'? Work on it.

Vox pops post lox,
Boris

Dear Dominic,
Read your blog. You've got a line in it about 'the likes of Goldman Sachs writing cheques for Remain'. I just wonder if any of the you-know-whos might jump down our throats about that one. You know how they are.
Limbo in sepsis,
Boris

Dear Dominic,
We've got to get our story straight: am I the vote-winning charmer who squeezes support out of the least likely bod merely by the flick of my hair? Or am I the dodgy sod ducking out of interviews at the drop of a hat?
Urethra pendulum,
Boris

Dear Dominic,
Would you have a word in my Dad's ear? It's vital that we keep him off the screens as much as possible. I have absolutely no objection to what he's saying. It's just that i don't want people to hear it.
Pater cloaca est,
Boris

Dec 1, 2019

Dear Dominic,
I'm not sure TV is really my thing. I can't expand into my jovial, Latin-quoting, bon viveur self. Could you please work your magic and ensure that I don't get caught on there again? That nice Nick on the radio is more my style.
Ferrari bonus est,
Boris

Dec 1, 2019

Dear Dominic,
Am doing tricky juggling act: trying to say that some stuff we didn't do in the last 9 years, is Labour's fault. Does anyone believe the baloney that falls out of my mouth? Victory beckons.
Nonsensia salami,
Boris

On the Today Programme with Holly Willoughby, Philip Schofield cornered Jeremy Corbyn by saying: "This is your opportunity to apologise to the Jewish community." He did not listen to Jeremy Corbyn's explanations. An enquiry into the matter found there was no reason for an apology from Mr. Corbyn.

Dec 3, 2019

Dear Dominic,
I see that the good man Philip Schofield went on and on at Corbyn to get him to apologise about the stuff he says about Jew boys. Now let's get someone to ask him why he didn't apologise earlier.
Post hydrangea in ventilator fixit,
Boris

Dec 4, 2019

Dear Dominic,
The success of our campaign should be measured by
the extent to which we've got the media to paint Corbyn
as 'the problem' and not on anything to do with policy. I
can't find my trousers.
Ad hominem ad nauseam,
Boris

**Boris Johnson avoided television interviews during the days
before the election. He was particularly keen to avoid Andrew
Neil who nevertheless broadcast the questions he would have
asked him.**

Dec 5, 2019

Dear Dominic,
What the hell is going on? I thought Andrew Neil could
be relied on? He's put out a video pretty well debagging
me in public. I am being bullied. I think I will ring Matron.
Terror in Rectum,
Boris

**On December the 11th, Boris Johnson visited a dairy in West
Yorkshire. A journalist and camera crew went to interview him
and it was said that Boris Johnson avoided them by dodging
into a commercial fridge.**

Dec 11, 2019

Dear Dominic,
Count to a hundred. See if you can find me? Hah! Used
to play that in the togs room. (It was blooming cold in
that fridge!) Anyway gimme a shout when I can come
out!
Occludo salmonella,

Boris

The General Election was held on Dec 12, 2019. The Conservative Party won with 365 seats to Labour's 202. Nigel Farage's UKIP party formed an alliance and did not field candidates in those seats where Conservatives did not have a secure majority. The election gave the Conservatives a majority of 80 seats.

Dec 15, 2019

Dear Dominic,
You told me to read someone called - I think - John Keans Maynard. So what we do now is do things that nearly everyone in our Party, since Thatcher, have said were wrong? Fair enough.
Taurus excrementus,
Boris

Dec 15, 2019

Dear Dominic,
When do we take Moggy out of moth balls? Genius to have kept him holed up in the cricket pavilion. Warmer than the blooming fridge, I bet. Lucky thing that my novel didn't make the headlines - some of it was a bit over-egged I confess.
Frigorifico testes,
Boris

Dec 24, 2019

Dear Dominic,
Sozz I didn't warn you we're dashing to Musters. You've played a blinder - thank goodness you kept me away from Neil. Is there any chance of getting rid of the archive of old Taki's articles from the time I was editor?
Caesar Boris

Dec 24, 2019

Dear Dominic,
Look, I really don't want to have to come back to Blighty
till mid-Jan, so anything you can do to keep the lions at
bay, greatly received. You probs can't do anything about
the weather though. Joke. Does Gove need to exist?
Europa Excrementa est,
Boris

PART II 2020

A VIRUS VISITS BRITANNIA

Ad absurdum ad nausea
(and getting lots of Brexit done)

Boris Johnson and Carrie Symmonds are now installed in Number 10 Downing Street. They left for a holiday on December 24th to celebrate the Conservative party's decisive general election win and New Year. They went to Mustique, a small island in the Caribbean.

Jan 3, 2020

Dear Dominic,
What's going on? We were just having a port on the verandah and some blithering twit from the FO was on asking me for some statement or other. Can't the geographically challenged Raab step up? The port is the 1932 you gave me.
Inebrio con brio,
Boris

On 3rd January, an Iranian Major General was killed by a US drone strike at Baghdad International airport. Donald Trump, President of the United States stated that the general was "directly and indirectly responsible for the deaths of millions of people." He included citizens of the United States in further statements. The all-powerful leader of Iran, the Ayatollah Khamenei threatened retribution. Iran went into mourning for the General.

Jan 4, 2020

Dear D,
Can I clarify: was Raab told? Was Priti told? Was Moggy told? Was Sajid told? Oh - hang on, I'm getting it: you were told weren't you? The White House think you're in charge so they bloody told you, didn't they? Reply by return.
In paranoia tango,
Boris

Jan 4, 2020

Dear D,
When we get back in a few weeks' time, which one of
Winston's would be best to dust down and re-use? The
beaches? The few? End of the beginning? Chicken, neck?
Advise.
Pro forma in dorma,
Boris

Jan 4, 2020

Dear Dom,
I'll need another one of your phrases for this skirmish
with the Persians: Get the War done...Get Iran run
over...Get the tin hats on...Get in and get out...Get on
down...Get on it...(Not sure I'm doing this right. Over to
you.
Peleponnesia amnesia,
Boris

Jan 5, 2020

Dear Dominic,
Got a set of blooming buttons in a suitcase thing here. I
think I'm up to speed on it but I'm not 100% au fait with
what each of them connects to. Does the red one send
over the Spitfires? Hah! Just kidding. Kind of. Anyway -
send plan asap.
Veni vidi didi,
Boris

Jan 6, 2020

Dear Dominic,
How's me hanging on in Mustard for a few more days
going down in Blighty? I can't believe that there are
moaners and groaners complaining about it. Surely
what people love about me is that I'm just a fun guy?
Anything going on in Iran?
Non cognoscenti,
Boris

Jan 6, 2020

Dear Dominic,
On beach wondering if Iraq or Iran could be a Brexit
dividend for us? Could you do one of your brilliant back-
of-the-envelope diagrams and see if there's all sorts of
British stuff we could flog out there? Melton Mowbray
pies? Eccles cakes?
Post prandium gloria,
Boris

Jan 7, 2020

Dear Dominic,
How's old Taki? Now the election's over I think we three
could have a discreet meet in a Mayfair watering hole. I
miss his acerbic chats. I'll be dressed as Bono. Don't
want the paps to spot me.
Incognito nintendo,
Boris

Jan 7, 2020

Dear Dominic,
I gather people don't know where I am. To tell the truth, I
don't know either. Got separated from the squeeze. I
really don't recognise this flat and I don't want to go out
in case someone spots me. Have you got the Russia
report or have I?
Avocado hospitalis,
Boris

**When journalists went to Downing Street on the 3rd February,
for a briefing by David Frost, the Prime Minister's Europe
adviser, names were called out dividing them into two groups.
One group was asked to leave, presumably because they were
critical of government policy. In the end all the journalists left
in protest. Questions were asked in parliament.**

Feb 3, 2020

Dear Dominic,
Good work chucking out stroppy journalists today. Most
of them too big for their boots, anyway. Can you check if
they're all Brits and/or with settled status. Would be
good to get some out of the way altogether.
Expulsiones detritus,
Boris

**Sajid Javid served as Chancellor of the Exchequer from July
2019 until the 13th February 2020 when, in a cabinet reshuffle,
Boris Johnson asked Javid to get rid of his team of aides. Javid
refused to do so and instead offered his resignation.**

Feb 14, 2020

Dear Dominic,
Sent Sajid Wotsit a box of choccies to sugar the pill, but
then, panicko momento: do Indians eat chocolates? I

thought, oh no, not another letterboxgate! Anyway, any
ideas for who might give the squeeze and me a decent
Easter lodging?
Taverna delicioso,
Boris

**Dominic Cummings had appointed a young man called Andrew
Sabisky as an adviser to the Conservative party who some
years earlier had written an article endorsing what appeared
to be the 'science' of eugenics.**

Feb 17, 2020

Dear Dominic,
What did you make of my genome? I think it looks pretty
damned good but I'm not as up on these things as your
Swarovski chap.
Genetico modificationis,
Boris

Feb18, 2020

Dear Dominic,
Very sorry you've had to let your man Saponsky go.
Don't take it personally but I had too many of the new
wave saddo MPs hunting him down. Keep your head
down for a bit, eh?
In mega excrementum,
Boris

Feb 18, 2020

Dear Dominic,
Looks like we're getting away with it: not much fuss
about Satrotsky at all. Who shall we hire instead? Jim
Davidson?
Opera buffo,
Boris

Dear Dominic,
Where are you? I fear the public wrath over Sikorsky has reached the Tiber and threatening Rome. Talking of inundations, I hear there's a lot of it in some northern parts. I need some good quotes to stem the tide.
Tempo fuctit,
Boris

Between November 2019 and February 2020, severe flooding occurred across the UK. Dr Simon Parry, a hydrologist said that February was, "a truly remarkable month in hydrological terms". There were peak flow records on many rivers. A 'Tory party supporter of many years' was on the news asking for something to be done in Shropshire.

Dear supporter,
Chin up, old chap. Think of it as if it's going punting. We did plenty of it when I was at Oxford. Why not put your subscription to the Conservative Party on to Direct Debit?
Aqua gargantua non problemo,
Boris

Dear Dominic,
I'm getting a bit of a roasting for not turning up in some of these places where there are a few more puddles than usual. Maybe you could put in an appearance? People seem to like you.
Persona non stata,
Boris

Mar 7, 2020

Dear Dominic,
Have you got the hang of this Croonervirus yet? If we get
a cough and stuff, why do we have to wash our hands?
Matron gave us some godawful linctus but you sure
went out there and played rugger after a dose of that.
Will tell Matt Upcock.
Respiratio non plus,
Boris

Mar 10, 2020

Dear Dominic,
How many people do you think we can let die before
there are riots? Drop me a line on it after the weekend,
the squeeze and I are off for a scoot round the Channel
Islands.
Post mortem post partum,
Boris

Mar 11, 2020

Dear Dominic,
We're going to spaff trillions in the budget. I need to get
out of the jam that people are going to say I've turned
into Corbyn. Send over some words for the press to use
about me instead of 'deficit', 'spendthrift' and
'communist'.
Financia fantasia,
Boris

Mar 13, 2020

Dear Dominic,
I think I may be in error. When I said that perhaps one
way to deal with this coronary virus is take it on the chin,
that's because I thought it's how the virus works:
whacks you on the chin. Anything I should be reading?
Erratum patum peperium,
Boris

Mar 13, 2020

Dear Dominic,
Been chatting with the chaps from 'The Sun' and we
want to put it to you the idea of running a campaign in
which we do a mock-up of the viruses wearing
swastikas and Hitler moustaches. And we're
divebombing them with our Spitfires. Thoughts?
Isolatio fellatio,
Boris

Mar 15, 2020

Dear Dominic,
This virus thingy is getting to be a bit of bore. Why don't
we create a Virus Tsar and he can do all these blooming
press conferences? Matt Talkcock is a disaster. He
sounds less convincing than a turnip. And no Rugby for
god's sake!
Corona mona,
Boris

Mar 15, 2020

Dear Dominic,
I fear we're losing control of the narrative here. (I don't
know what that means but I've heard people like you say

it so I'm saying it too.) Look, tell me straight, is this convolvulus thing a big baddie or not?
Delirium tremendens,
Boris

Mar 16, 2020

Dear Dominic,
Some of our chaps in the Lords are pretty decrepit. High risk. Any suggestions on what to do with them? Be discreet.
Mausoleum superba,
Boris

Mar 16, 2020

Dear Dominic,
When do we get rid of Matt Talkcock? He's suffering from foot in mouth disease. Cull him. I'm off to the country with the squeeze. Anything going on I should know about?
Pesto infesto,
Boris

From this point on the author was not able to continue writing as he contracted Covid-19. He might not have been able to tweet again in the future except for the amazing love and care he received from family, friends and the NHS staff. You can read about this episode of his life in 'Many Different Kinds of Love'.

Sep 9, 2020

Dear Dominic,
I've got this big idea: test and trace. What do you think? I
got it from a woman I overheard when my driver
stopped at a traffic light. She was saying she couldn't
get a Covid test. I thought: let's do it!
Magnum opus dopus,
Boris

Sep 9, 2020

Dear Boris,
I see you're thinking of chucking some serious dosh at
the testing prob. I run a small firm that sells silver cups
to schools and sporting clubs. I think we could do the
job. Btw we went to the same college.
[not signed]

Nov 11, 2020

Dear Dominic,
Do you have a store of metaphors about your person?
Did you hear my cavalry and bugles stuff the other day?
Glorious, eh? I've switched to boxing. Do you know the
Eton Wall Game? I was damned good at it. Would that
work?
Vaxo vaxinus in wallo wallorum,
Boris

Nov 12, 2020

Dear Dominic,
You may have heard rumours that you're on the way out.
Don't believe them, dear chap. Take my word for it and
you know my word is my bond. Don't I always tell the
truth?

Exit poco homo,
Boris

Dear Dominic,
Afraid the squeeze gave me an ultimatum and it's no time to break the distaff. Future meet-ups in camera, OK?
Vivat rex et dolce vita,
Boris

Dear Dominic,
I dreamed about you last night. You were in a car, beetling up the motorway, police were chasing you, calling out to you through a megaphone, 'Your time's up Number 3!' Anyway, see you on the other side, when I've jacked in this awful job.
In nocte pollo,
Boris

Dear Dominic,
I'm hearing on the airwaves that you're telling people you were leaving anyway. Given that we are looking at a parting of the ways, I suggest you should avoid a deficit on the truth balance. That deficit is my privilege.
Veritas non pesto,
Boris

Nov 22, 2020

Dear Dominic,
Miss you! Am writing this in the cupboard out of sight of
the squeeze - you know her views on the Dom! Say no
more. Non plus dixit! I boobed on the devolution front
but I channelled a Cummings boat hook to get me out of
that!
Priti in excretio extracta,
Boris

Nov 24, 2020

Dear Dominic,
I'm writing to you unintentionally. Be discreet. This
correspondence is not taking place. Any advice on what
to do with the stroppy backbenchers? It's not that I
disagree with them. It's just a matter of getting them to
shut up about it.
Discordia prosecco,
Boris

Nov 25, 2020

Dear Dominic,
Christmas is galloping over the brow of the hill blowing
its festive bugle. Do you think my Xmas message has
been clear? 'Meet, mix but not too much, be jolly, but not
jolly close. Open windows, close mouths.'
Ad absurdum ad nausea,
Boris

Nov 25, 2020

Dear Dominic,
One all night sesh we had playing Monopoly in college,
and the banker ran out of money. We just wrote out

more notes and it worked fine. Should I tell Rish?
Financibus ad infinitum,
Boris

Nov 26, 2020

Dear Dominic,
What do you think of our financial thingummy? We're
whacking jonny foreigner and the toiling masses in one
fell swoop. (Or in one foul swipe, as 'Goebbels', my Latin
master used to call it.) By the way, we don't actually
borrow money, do we?
Minus plus toto zero,
Boris

Nov 28, 2020

Dear Dominic,
These tier thingies have me somewhat baffled. Am
hoping the tribunes don't bloody come a-knocking on
my door hoping I can explicate. What tier are you in? Or
will you be barnarding again?
Fusilli inferno,
Boris

Dec 5, 2020

Dear Dominic,
Am stuck in a room with some frightful Euro-maiden. I
think I'm supposed to be negotiating something. Not
sure what. I've got a note reminding me I should be
rooting for our fish. Rule the waves, eh?
Pisces britannicus,
Boris

Many Brexit supporters saw the control of fishing rights as a symbol of regained sovereignty. Dominic Raab, Foreign Secretary said: "On fishing there is a point of principle: as we leave the EU we're going to be an independent…costal state and we've got to be able to control our waters." However, the most popular catches in the UK are mackerel and herring, not enjoyed much by the UK population so these catches were being sold to EU countries.

Dec 6, 2020

Dear Dominic,
'Tomorrow creeps in this pretty place till the last syllabus of reordered time.' A bit of the bard for you there! Still thinking about our silver friends beneath the azure main. What if tomorrow I let them have the haddock and we keep the cod?
Omnivorus omnibus,
Boris

Dec 8, 2020

Dear Dominic,
I miss your snappy slogans. To be honest I'm floundering around a bit with the metaphorology: level playing field, brow of the hill, down in the dumps, the sunny uplands, up in the air, up the sally alley (did I just make that up?)
Mens sana in corpore sago,
Boris

Dec 9, 2020

Dear Dominic,
Could do with a brief refresh. What actually is sovereignty? I know we wanted it. Did we get it? Or is it that I'm trying to get it?
Caveat casa vendor,
Boris

On the 9th December Boris Johnson went to Brussels to meet
Ursula von der Leyen, President of the European Commission,
for what was seen as potentially a last chance to break the im-
passe on talks on a trade deal.

Dec 9, 2020

Dear Dominic,
Am in Brussels. Where you? Barnard Wotsit? Am
starving. They haven't dished up the tuck yet. Hope it'll
be Belgian bangers. Must get Gove to serve me some
back in Blighty.
Porcus in excelsis deo,
Boris
PS how many sprogs have I got? (In case Frau Brussels
asks me)

Dec 10, 2020

Dear Dominic,
Am bored off my trotters. All I can hear is the maids in
the corridors yakking in unintelligible babble. Have been
playing Rumsfield's card game 'Churchill Solitaire'. Try it,
dear chap. Missing you.
Solo nolo me tangere,
Boris

Dec 13, 2020

Dear Dominic,
Got to ring Frau Europe later today. This is the Persians
facing the Athenians at Dunkirk. Either they put the egg
in the scrum or they don't. Wish you were here to stick it
to them.
Interim in pasta,
Boris

Dec 13, 2020

Dear Dominic,
I'm slowly coming to the conclusion that the prob with foreigners is that they're foreign. They keep trying to do things their way. I've done everything I can to show them that they're wrong but they won't listen.
Omnibus terminus,
Boris

Dec 14, 2020

Dear Dominic,
Were you in the scouts, dear boy? We used to sing, 'Here we sit like birds in the wilderness (repeat repeat) down in Demerara.' Could have been written for me this week. Am I going to be known for the biggest balls-up since Suez?
Ego in cloaca est,
Boris

Dec 14, 2020

Dear Dominic,
Yawn yawn. Dunno how much longer we've got to stretch out this charade. Fish fish fish. Can't stand the stuff unless it's hidden in port-drenched batter and I've sploshed mayo all over it. Have you been to Brussels? What's that giant molecule?
Ad hoc hic hic,
Boris

Dec 18, 2020

Dear Dominic,
Do you have any idea what Liz Truss is on about? Who is this Foucuald? Is he one of Barnier's amigos? Which tier

are you in? Buggered if I know which one I'm in. Will you be in Barnard Wotsit? So many questions. Missing you.
Chaos intacta,
Boris

Dec 19, 2020

Dear Dominic,
Who first said, 'My indecision is final'? It's beginning to haunt me. Actually, it doesn't matter what I do or say because Starmer's indecision is even more final than mine. Missing you.
Oscillato permanente,
Boris

Dec 23, 2020

Dear Dominic,
Now the blooming scientists have invented some kind of turbocharged super virus that flies about like a jet fighter and that evil little squit Macron is closing his borders. We close borders. Not them. Who do they think they are?
Anus finis,
Boris

Dec 25, 2020

Dear Dominic,
Am in shed to get away from the brat bawling. Am going to have to keep this 'sovereignty' thing going over the next four years. Will Red Wall Man start moaning soon? I'll just have to bang on about Melton Mowbray pies or something. Yawn.
Anglia ganglia,
Boris

Dec 28, 2020

Dear Dominic,
People digging up my Greenwich speech to prove I
wasn't tooled up for this Covid wotsit. Confess: I was
rather hoping it to be my Churchill 'Iron Curtain'
moment, thus the floridity but it looks like I was saying
poo to safety measures.
In memoriam mortem,
Boris

Dec 29, 2020

Dear Dominic,
Hand on heart, dear boy, we're up to our eyeballs in the
proverbial here. I so wish you were here to keep the
caravanserai on the road. If only Oxford Analytica had
jumped to it more speedily with their vaccine.
Pestilentia non pesto,
Boris

Dec 30, 2020

Dear Dominic,
We're going to keep some of the schools open some of
the time some of the schools not open some of the time,
all the schools partially open and partially closed with
some schools half-open and other schools half closed.
Gove is handling it.
Scholasticus elasticus,
Boris

Dec 30, 2020

Dear Dominic,
What is a virus? Talking to someone who much admires
me, told me Covid doesn't exist. He had some pretty
cogent arguments and I found I was lacking in the
wherewithal to answer him. Come back to me on the
secret email: squeeze has banned you.
Ludo in gloria,
Boris

Dec 31, 2020

Dear Dominic,
Had some blooming consultant on zoom moaning on
and on about how his Intensive Care Unit gone from one
nurse per bed to one nurse per 6 beds. Felt like saying,
'Jolly good. Productivity up,' but said we were working
on it. We're not, of course.
Minus plus est,
Boris

PART III 2021

INTERNATIONAL GATHERINGS IN BRITANNIA

Veritas in cloaca
(Still getting lots of Brexit done)

'You boy! Did you wash your hands before handling that ball?

Jan 1, 2021

Dear Dominic,
Thought we'd kick off the new year with a flourish. A re-set, if you like. We've decided to keep primary schools open. Sorry, as you were: closed. That is, open in a closed sort of a way. Secondary schools will be both open and closed.
Occludo ludo,
Boris

Jan 1, 2021

Dear Dominic,
We're having larks havin' Gavin at the moment. We push him out in front of the nation's press, get him to make a statement about what's going to happen, while behind his back we've worked out a completely opposite policy. Covid fun, eh?
Superbus me,
Boris

Jan 2, 2021

Dear Dominic,
We've finally got a clear policy: we're closing London schools because they're in London. Newcastle schools are not in London so we're not closing them. If they were in London we would close them. But they're not. So we're not closing them.
Clarificatio faeces,
Boris

Jan 3, 2021

Dear Dominic,
I think it would help if we made all schools into boarding schools. Send the kids off, keep the staff on site. No

mixing with outside world. Et voilà! Sorted. I'll get Gove
to work on it. He's good at schools stuff. Missing you.
Iuvenilia memorabilia,
Boris

Jan 3, 2021

Dear Dominic,
When matron brought my hot choccy in the dorm, used
to ask her to experiment with different flavours: golden
syrup, marmite... Some nights, no choccy. Never did me
any harm. It's like that with the vaccines: mix'em up,
leave gaps. No harm done.
Non mea culpa,
Boris

Jan 4, 2021

Dear Dominic,
Have you seen Gavin? Gavin Williamson. He's in
Education under the heel of Gibb. Have you seen him? Is
he with you? Or is he trying to offload some old
fireplaces? I need someone to blather about exams
instead of me.
Flexus in plexus,
Boris

Jan 6, 2021

Dear Dominic,
People are digging up past clips of me saying that
schools are safe and then another one of me talking
about 'vectors'. Let's be clear: I don't know what a vector
is so I can't be held to account for saying there's a
vector. Is a vector a virus?
Solo in polo,
Boris

In the United States, Joe Biden had been elected President with the democrats winning the 2020 election. On January 6th 2021 a mob of Trump supporters, convinced that the election had been 'stolen', marched from the White House, where they had listened to Trump speaking, to the Capitol. There they overcame security guards, breached locked gates and doors and threatened to kill Vice President Pence to prevent him carrying out his duty of officially recording the newly elected president. Mike Pence was hastily removed from the building.

Jan 7, 2021

Dear Dominic,
Have to confess, I thought Trump was quite the joker. Liked the cut of his jib and he certainly put the wind up the sails of the global elite. No bad thing. I'm distancing myself now though, of course. You should too. Am I in the global elite?
Rectum imperfectum,
Boris

Jan 7, 2021

Dear Dominic,
Having to keep Moggy out of sight at the moment. He was quite enamoured of El Trumpissimo. He even called on Americans to 'vote Trump'. Don't want the media unearthing that one tvm. In fact, Moggy is best when he's muted.
Alfa romeo bonus,
Boris

Jan 10, 2021

Dear Dominic,
I'm having dreams of some election soon which we lose and some of our more, shall we say 'active' supporters,

refuse to accept it and storm Westminster. I hear myself urging them on in Latin. You're there in a crash helmet with a bazooka.
Militia somnambula,
Boris

Jan 11, 2021

Dear Dominic,
The moaners and wingers are on about me going for a bike ride now. How else am I supposed to get away from the thing? It's teething now. And the nanny won't come near us because she says we haven't had the jab. She's foreign.
Regis bognor non cyrille,
Boris

Jan 13, 2021

Dear Dominic,
Am trying to find a way of keeping news of death rates in Taiwan, New Zealand, South Korea etc away from all these news hounds. Comparisons are odious. Missing you.
Stoma romana,
Boris

Jan 14, 2021

Dear Dominic,
The advantage of keeping hopeless Gavin on is that it distracts from how hopeless I am. He's wittering on now about how exams are on. Or off. Bit like me saying one day schools are safe and the next that they are vectors of infection.
Convolvulus involvulus,
Boris

Jan 19, 2021

Dear Dominic,
So Trump walks. My latest wheeze, when Cabinet zoom meetings get boring is to slap on a slide of the picture taken of Gove saying gratters to Trump for getting elected. Guffaws all round and Gove goes pink. Missing you.
Tedium ad medium,
Boris

Jan 21, 2021

Dear Dominic,
I really need some advice, dear boy. Gavin Williamson is the other side of useless and of course he's for the choppo but I can't sack him or I'll look beyond useless for not sacking him earlier. Cleft stick. Scylla and Charybdis. Bog.
In lavatorio tori,
Boris

Jan 21, 2021

Dear Dominic,
What is this flapdoodle about awarding Covid contracts to our friends? It's what friends are for: we help each other. It's mutual consideration. If ever I was short of the readies, I would expect Dido et al to give me a hand. Why not?
Remuneratio ad infinitum,
Boris

Jan 31, 2021

Dear Dominic,
It doesn't matter what we screw up, we stay ahead in

the polls. To tell the truth, dear boy, it all feels like a bit of a jape. Don't hear from you at all. Where dost thou lurk? Not Chez Barnard, perhaps? Missing you.
Synthesis pubis,
Boris

Feb 4, 2021

Dear Dominic,
What do you think of my clapping? Good,eh? I watched a clip of me doing it and if I had to rate myself I'd say that I do it with sincerity and style. In short, I'm a good clapper. Watch out Covid, I'm going to clap you to hell.
Pro patria Toyota,
Boris

Feb 7, 2021

Dear Dominic,
Am lying low. As opposed to just lying! The proverbial is hitting the fan from all directions what with DUP spotting that there actually is a border in the Irish Sea - damn I thought I'd hidden it, and someone letting the SA mutation rip.
Tibia rex,
Boris

Feb 8, 2021

Dear Dominic,
See me! I go out there and tell the world what's going on with jabs, viruses, mutations, variants as if I'm Mr hot shot epidemiologist. I'm Winston raising the nation's morale: never has so much been lost by so many thanks to so few. (Is that it?)
Sub cervix,
Boris

Feb 14, 2021

Dear Dominic,
The good news is burying the bad. It's all wall to wall vaccine and that bloomin' death toll is finally off the front pages. Result for Bojo, or what, dear boy? I'm coming out of this morass smelling of roses and lashings of Chanel No 5.
Doner immobile,
Boris

Matt Hancock was Secretary of State for Health. He promoted the government's policies during lockdown of keeping a safe distance from those who were not in your family while having an affair at work where, clearly, he was not keeping a safe distance.

Feb 19, 2021

Dear Dominic,
Hancock's just been fried. Nice to see that he's taking the hit for the team. After all, when your prop gouges out the opposite prop's eye, it's not the captain who gets sent off. As Rugger, as life. Missing you.
Ludo in excelsis dildo,
Boris

Feb 22, 2021

Dear Dominic,
Just between you and me, I've got myself stuck in the old Scylla Charybdis prob: I'm on record saying, schools are safe and schools are spreaders. I think I'll say that in fact they are 'safe spreaders'. What do you think?
Dilemma inflagrante,
Boris

Feb 22, 2021

Dear Dominic,
Do you see me being magnificent in the House today? Gone are the days, O Achilles, when we used to chew over my performances back in Numero Ten. Luckily, I can rely on Starmer to fire paper arrows. I say, 'Schools will open' and they open.
De facto paxo,
Boris

Feb 23, 2021

Dear Dominic,
I hope you are being rigorous with the whole masking, social distancing caboodle. I'm certainly sticking to rigid restrictions with my MPs. As for the rest of the country: quod ego dico, non ut faciam (Do as I say, or you'll end up in the doodoo).
Rigor mortis,
Boris

Feb 25, 2021

Dear Dominic,
I'm looking into the idea of insisting that all schools run Latin summer camps. Broached the matter with Gove, who's keen. Williamson will agree to anything. He knows he's a hairsbreadth from the chop anyway. Missing you desperately.
Cobra absentia,
Boris

Feb 25, 2021

Dear Dominic,
For years Gibb et al have been banging on about how exams are fairer than teacher assessment, and now I'm telling the bloody masses that teachers doing it is fair. What if it is fair? It'll stymie us for beating the drums for exams next year.
Circus in tandem,
Boris

Mar 1, 2021

Dear Dominic,
Bloody hell, Cameron has come out of his garden shed

to start delivering lectures on what I should or should not be doing. Captains who leave sinking ships should face trial. Mind you, if went down that road, I'd end up in the Tower!
Ad infinitum bitum,
Boris

Mar 3, 2021

Dear Dominic,
Should I keep an eye on Rishi? "Let me have men about me that are fat, sleek-headed me and as sleep a-nights. Yond Cassius has a lean and hungry look. He thinks too much. Such men are dangerous."
Proxima pox,
Boris

In 2020 Priti Patel, the Home Secretary came under scrutiny for bullying civil servants in her department. In November of that year a cabinet office enquiry found that she had breached the ministerial code. Thus, in March 2021, a former high level civil servant was paid out a considerable sum by the government in a settlement of a claim for constructive dismissal.

Mar 4, 2021

Dear Dominic,
Did you see that we've paid off that mandarin fellow who was whingeing about getting a wigging from the gorgeous Priti? What a wet. We sloshed some dosh all over him and we won't hear a peep from him. Not my dosh, so I'm not bothered.
Silentio bentio,
Boris

Mar 9, 2021

Dear Dominic,
I've got away with it! I told them schools are opening but
people will get infected and hardly a peep from the usual
pessimists and naysayers. Public numbness is the new
black and I'm riding high in the polls. Ever onwards.
Corona bona,
Boris

Mar 12, 2021

Dear Dominic,
I am overbloodyjoyed to be in a position to say the Elgin
bloody Marbles are ours. If there's one thing that makes
me proud to be British it's knowing our forbears got hold
of stuff like that and rendered it unto the British Caesar.
Gloria in excelsis oreo,
Boris

Mar 25, 2021

Dear Dominic,
Did you catch my bantz about 'capitalism and greed'?
Foot in the proverbial, eh?! And the Woke are making hay
out of it, of course. Did you say once that if a few oldies
die, 'too bad', or was that a Private Eye concoction?
Missing you.
Gratis non grappa,
Boris

Mar 29, 2021

Dear Dominic,
Allegra is keeping the press hounds at bay over the
Italian job. Did you see la signora has blabbed to the
press about where and when - everything apart from the

colour of my boxers. As for the dosh - blithering fuss over pennies.
Coitus intercorruptus,
Boris

Mar 30, 2021

Dear Dominic,
Sometimes I hug myself for the sheer nerve of me! What do the you-know-whose call it? Chutzpah? I've just joined an international demand for us all to 'learn the lessons' of the pandemic. I'm the one stopping an enquiry here! Boris the eel!
Mucus in elipsis,
Boris

Apr 11, 2021

Dear Dominic,
Gav's going big on discipline, thanks to Gibb. Little Gibb (Giblet) - always there, never promoted. He's Mr Slipper in the cupboard who comes out to whack teachers. Bit worried that the press will look at my disciplinary record at school.
Juvenilia horribilis,
Boris

Apr 19, 2021

Dear Dominic,
I am so busy with this Super Soccer League thingy. I've cleared my desk of everything else. I think the British people love their soccer and Allegra says that me looking concerned about this will massage the ratings. Furrowed brow time!
Veritas in cloaca,
Boris

Apr 20, 2021

Dear Dominic,
I sent Little Gav out to face the Today mob. He wittered on about his beloved soccer club - I've forgotten which one it is already. Local? Hah! People will be demanding I stick up for 'local' libraries and post offices next!
Ludus lupus,
Boris

Apr 20, 2021

Dear Dominic,
I've only gone and done it. I can see the headlines: Boris Saves Soccer! I only had to stand at that podium and ramp up the oratory for the whole edifice to come tumbling down. I added a few Os to my vote tally with that, my man.
Samson ludorum,
Boris

Apr 21, 2021

Dear Dominic,
Did you see my stentorian performance in the House? We will bang back at milksop Starmer again and again, 'Sleaze? What sleaze?' Could do with a snappy slogan from you, tho. 'Get sleaze done!' or some such.
Mammon gammonorum,
Boris

Apr 23, 2021

Dear Dominic,
Treason has done his worst. Fair is foul, foul is fair. Et tu, Brute. Whether 'tis nobler in the mind to suffer the slings and arrows of outrageous fortune or to take up arms

against a sea of troubles. The isle is full of noises.
Furioso avocado,
Boris

Apr 23, 2021

Dear Dominic,
I could have crushed you like a peanut on a railway track
but spared you. What do I get in return? Treachery.
Remember, you miserable little weasel, we all have
skeletons in our cupboards and you have them in a lot of
other places too.
Casus belli pirelli,
Boris

Apr 24, 2021

Dear Dominic,
Am chortling you say I'm 'totally unethical'. Have you
only just discovered this? You read my novel, 'Seventy-
two Virgins'. It's a completely amoral bit of work, packed
to the gunnels with racist, antisemitic and sexist gags
and I'm proud of it!
Sordidus ego,
Boris

Apr 26, 2021

Dear Dominic,
Pick up! You're not replying to me. You must see what's
going on: they're using this hoohah about the squeeze's
refurb as their way to drop the pilot. The dark forces
want me out. I'm in need of your acuity, dear boy. Pick
up!
Gastro impasto,
Boris

Apr 27, 2021

Dear Dominic,
They're on to me now about me saying let the virus rip.
I'll deny it of course, but who put me up to that idea, eh?
But of course you won't get the rap. You're probably in
Barnard bloody Castle and that's the brat screaming
again nw.
Silentum in lavatorium,
Boris

Apr 27, 2021

Dear Boris Johnson,
You said that GCSE exams for this year were cancelled.
They're not cancelled. They're called 'assessments'. And

instead of examiners marking them, teachers are. For no money. But the schools have paid the exam boards. Where's the money?
Yours,
Michael Rosen

Apr 28, 2021

Dear Dominic,
In the midst of my travails, the orange lady has dropped anchor. There's been muttering in the Masonic halls about loyalty and the eternal union. All my fault apparently. But she's gone first! Hah!
Williamus Rex problemus est,
Boris

Apr 29, 2021

Dear Dominic,
Well, you can be proud of yourself: you've given the other side the stick to beat me with. All I hear is flattety, flattety, flat. What does it bloody matter anyway? Caesar's toga is more luxurious that that worn by the plebs - or indeed you.
In lux gaudeamus,
Boris

Apr 30, 2021

Dear Dominic,
Thanks to you, all attention is focussed on the squeeze as if it's her fault that we gave the place a lick of paint. Remember: I saved the country from Covid. I won the Battle of Britain 2021. What goes on behind closed doors is my affair.
De bello phallico,
Boris

French fisherman were threatening to blockade the harbour at Jersey as the government of Jersey was refusing to license French boats to fish in Jersey waters. The UK sent two patrol boats as Jersey is a Crown dependency. However, the matter was eventually resolved amicably between Jersey island and the French fishing authorities.

May 5, 2021

Dear Dominic,
Jeepers creepers, la not-so-belle France have declared war. I forget that thing about Jersey - is it ours or theirs? Or both? Surely the micro-Corsican with the hat wouldn't have gone along with that. I'll send over a few Spitfires.
Casus belli dansa,
Boris

May 6, 2021

Dear Dominic,
Stuff the Entente Cordiale! Biff, bang, bosh as Nancy our old rugger master used to say. Gun boats on the horizon, the old Palmerston trick and perfect eve-of-election timing. Nothing we Brits love more than the sound of a cannon.
Mortem bonus est,
Boris

May 12, 2021

Dear Dominic,
Did you see I've OK'd the Covid inquiry? You'd better work out how you're going to tackle the rumour that was in the press that claimed you said, 'if some pensioners die, too bad' or some such. I'm working on 'my bodies piling up' gag.

Alibi ad lib,
Boris

Dominic Cummings was giving evidence to the select committee investigating the handling of the pandemic. His evidence of what was happening in government during February and March 2020 made it clear there was insufficient focus or planning on what the World Health Organisation was by then calling a 'public health emergency'.

May 23, 2021

Dear Dominic,
So you're going to open Pandora's box? I'll be Horatio on the bridge slashing through the Gordian Knot with the sword of Damocles. You're doing this after all I've done for the British people. Yes, after all I have done for the British people.
Memento genocide,
Boris

May 26, 2021

Dear Dominic,
I thought we had a deal: you stay in silentio, I stay in silentio. Luckily for me, the media are focussing on Carrie's dog. I will emerge like Atalanta's bull, riding Cerberus with the Nereides trilling to Achilles. You're dead meat.
Narcissus appendix,
Boris

May 26, 2021

Dear Dominic,

You haven't put a glove on me. I'll keep repeating: non mea culpa, dear Brutus, I did what I could. I will do my lonely puppy look and the plebs will go on adoring me. You, on the other hand, will be known forever as a weasel.

Rictus plexus,

Boris

May 27, 2021

Dear Dominic,

Your ghastly display yesterday in which you tried to turn the whole thing into a charivari of machiavellianism will fail. I will ensure that what happened will be seen as nothing more than occasional but understandable slip-ups. Die, worm, die!

Vivat Boris Rex,

Boris

May 27, 2021

Dear Dominic,

Aha, weasel! You thought you'd skewer me but my friends in the media are telling it like it's Mr Crazy trying to get revenge. Eastenders not Silent Witness. Boris jumps free yet again!

Homo eroicus,

Boris

May 29, 2021

Dear Dominic,
What did I say? You're not even yesterday's man, not
even the day before yesterday's man. You are the man
that time forgot. I will be remembered forever as the
hero who single-handedly vaccinated the nation.
Iniectiones albion,
Boris

Jun 6, 2021

Dear Dominic,
If only we could wind the clock back when it was just me
and you running the country. If only, if only. In the
meantime, I'm up against it over this 'catch up'
flapdoodle. Ah, if only you were here to get me out of it.
Nostalgia per neuralgia,
Boris

**The UK was hosting the G7 Conference. It was held at Carbis
Bay in Cornwall, near St Ives. The heads of government posed
for photographs with Boris standing next to Joe Biden. They
were seen walking together on the beach. It all looked idyllic.**

Jun 9, 2021

Dear Dominic,
While you piffle about looking for non-existent skeletons
in cupboards, I meet with the POTUS himself. Why, man,
I bestride the narrow world like a Colossus, and you
petty man, walk under my huge legs and peep about, to
find yourself a dishonorable grave.
Stupendus,
Boris

Jun 16, 2021

Dear Dominic,
We need to talk. OK, you know where the bodies are
buried. You forget your name is mud. People think you're
a cross between Rasputin and Machiavelli. And I've got
your emails to me. Even the one about...you know the
one. Let's do a deal.
Panic sub toga,
Boris

**Despite having been responsible for significant cuts to the na-
tional budget for museums, George Osborne was offered and
accepted the Chair of the British Museum.**

Jun 24, 2021

Dear Dominic,
Osborne's landed the BM jobby! There are of course
channels along which a PM's nod might be propelled. If
you and I hadn't fallen out, I might have come to an
arrangement for you not unlike the one I secured for la
dame italienne.
Considerata desiderata,
Boris

Jun 25, 2021

Dear Dominic,
Some of your media projects were spectacular. Perhaps
we could patch things up between us if you came up
with something new for us. I was thinking along the
lines of a Cabinet Love Island...half-naked shots of us all
by a pool? With masks?
In flagrante pante,
Boris

Jun 26, 2021

Dear Dominic,
It was you, wasn't it? You've been sitting on this video
for months, just biding your time like Horatio on the
bridge to slip it to Murdoch. Remember, Horatio was
defeated by Odysseus. Chaos miasma.
Gladiator in utero,
Boris

Jul 4, 2021

Dear Dominic,
I can't stand football. I think, for godssake pick the
bloody ball up, you ninnies. Seems like they've done
quite well even though they've all turned into marxists
doing this kneeling rubbish. I'll probs have to say, well
done, at some point.
Felicitato relucto,
Boris

Jul 5, 2021

Dear Dominic,
I could really do without your sniping from the wings. I'm
just about to liberate Britain from the flim-flam of Covid
constraints. I've figured the science: free of restrictions =
free of Covid. My slogan: 'Get done!' No, I mean, 'Get it
done!'.
Tex rex,
Boris

Jul 12, 2021

Dear Dominic,
Stepped in over this football stuff.I know it's pretty woke
of me, but there are limits.People are saying, 'Tu quoque'
but my stuff is banter.I didn't really think they were
letterboxes. I'm in favour of tolerance, especially
tolerance of me.
Ludi et rudi,
Boris

Jul 20, 2021

Dear Dominic,
I enjoyed your megalomaniac musing tonight but I
rather thought you gave the game away suggesting that
democracy is just something we game. It may be true
but that doesn't mean any of us should admit it.
Tabasco in glans,
Boris

Sep 17, 2021

Dear Dominic,
Long time non parlare. Just wanted to restart our
epistolary comms to say my reshuffers was inspired by
your memo re: Mavericks and oddballs. Any old jester
will do, I thought. After all, look at me!
In hysteria ad inferno,
Boris

Oct 13, 2021

Dear Dominic,
I see you're out yakking on about the NI Protocol and
now the Irish wotsit is up in arms going on about 'bad
faith' et cetera et cetera. Just because I called it the

Northern Ireland Protocock, doesn't give you the right to blab.
Hibernia cloaca est,
Boris

Oct 19, 2021

Dear Boris Johnson,
Why are other European countries showing better Covid figures than us? What are they doing right that we are doing wrong?
Yours,
Michael Rosen

In October the Commons Standard Committee found Owen Patterson to have "breached the rule prohibiting advocacy". They had found that he had used his position as an MP to secure benefits for companies who paid him considerable sums as a consultant. In November the government pushed back and put forward a motion to overturn Patterson's suspension. There was an outcry. Newspaper headlines were all accusing the prime minister of corruption as: 'rules on sleaze torn up.' Eventually Owen Patterson resigned as MP for North Shropshire.

Nov 6, 2021

Dear Jacob,
I'm taking a lot of flak for this darned Paterson affair so I'll have to find some servants willing to do a Brutus. Zac has offered me another weekend in the villa so I'm going to leave this with you. Talking of you, it could be you, of course.
Post mortem,
Boris

Nov 14, 2021

Dear Dominic,
The Tiber of scandal is rising and I may be washed
away. Can you muster a bit of meat to keep the hounds
at bay? You're good at coming up with something slick,
flashy and useless. Any ideas to help your old friend out?
Desperandum in faeces,
Boris

Nov 14, 2021

Dear Dominic,
We're having a go at something we've not tried before: herd impunity. In veritate, we've all been caught banging on the door of Croesus, yet think we can get away with it. And probs: we can!
Peccadillo piccalilli,
Boris

Nov 15, 2021

Dear Oliver,
Heard you battling with Robinson on Today, just now. Well done. You fended him off with torrents of meaningless garbage. My method to a T! You'll be applying for my job soon no doubt.
Mamma mea culpa,
Boris

When giving a speech at a Confederation of Business Industry conference, Boris Johnson amazed listeners by his fulsome praise of the Peppa Pig theme park which he had recently visited with his wife, Carrie and his young son, now one year old. He appeared to lose his notes at one point in his talk.

Nov 22, 2021

Dear Nadine,
Hope you caught my foray into culture: rooting for Peppa Pig. Did you see how I got in a dig at the BBC for turning it down? Ho bloody ho - I just made that bit up to annoy them. Thought you'd approve. When are you shutting them down?
Intoxicato embarrassamus,
Boris

News of parties at Downing Street during lockdown were circulating aided and abetted by information from Dominic Cummings.

Dec 2, 2021

Dear Sajid,
Put the lid on this Xmas party story, will you? Talk about the boosterfest or protein spikes or something. The wolves are circling like Christmas trees on the bridge over the Tiber. My grip is ever fast, doubt ye not.
Zeneca non Seneca,
Boris

Dec 7, 2021

Dear Rees-Mogg,
The two squirts who present I'm a Celebrity are targeting me. I will ask the fragrant Nadine to remind them that putting politics into Light Entertainment breaches guidelines and all breaches of guidelines on my watch are punished.
Terminus in excremento,
Boris

Dec 8, 2021

Dear Dominic,
I know that our ways have parted as did the Via Appia en route to Pompeii but I need a snappy comeback for PMQs today. They think they're going to BBQ me like a trussed pig but I will leap free. Any tips?
Motto in blotto,
Boris

Dec 8, 2021

Dear Priti,
We need one of your woke-shredding numbers pronto.
Can you rip into a) the metropolitan elite b) gypsies c)
the dinghy hordes? I caught a suggestion on the
wireless this morn about abolishing the Geneva
Convention on refugees. Run with it.
Distractio magnus,
Boris

Dec 8, 2021

Dear Fraser,
Over to you. I need a whopping great splash from you at
the Spectator to swing the guns 180 degrees. Mow
down anyone: Starmer, Gove, May, the Archbish. You
owe me. It's Xmas.
Quid pro quo hohoho,
Boris

Allegra Stratton resigned in tears from her job as senior government spokeswoman following public anger over a leaked video of her talking to staff in a joking way about holding a Christmas party at No 10 Downing Street on December 18th 2020 when London was under Tier 3 restrictions.

Dec 8, 2021

Dear Allegra,
Thanks for taking it for the team. We will of course be
able to remunerate you in the appropriate way. May I
also make a request? I think we are all agreed that
certain matters are best kept private.
Detritus in camera,
Boris

Dec 8, 2021

Dear Mogg,
With the exit of Allegra, I fear the Praetorian Guard is crumbling. Who is friend, who is foe? I foresee a future dragging my weary limbs round TV studios in order to sustain a decent level of appearance fee. Who is Cassius? Who is Brutus?
Sphinctus contractus,
Boris

Dec 8, 2021

Dear Austin and Mann,
I'm writing to you to express my gratitude for all you've done for me and the Party. In the eventuality of my departure, I leave with the wish that your high office should in no way be tarnished by events linked to my name.
Gloria in excelsis duo,
Boris

Downing Street director of communication, Jack Doyle is one of the highest government officials involved in the scandal surrounding Christmas parties in 2020 and the government is hoping his resignation will allay criticism.

Dec 10, 2021

Dear Jack,
Urgent. I need to know super pronto that you're going to carry the can on this. No shilly-shallying: you're the one holding the party popper, ok? Block. Neck. Yours. On. Eat this memo.
Urino maximo in toga,
Boris

Dec 10, 2021

Dear Rishi, Priti and Gove,
Where are you? I need you ramping it up on all news outlets, right now. Remember, I won you your jobs. You'd be howling at the moon if it wasn't for my immense joie de vivre, wit and common touch. Where are you?
Turbo pus in centrum,
Boris

Dec 10, 2021

Dear Truss,
I know your game, don't you worry. Think you're keeping your nose clean by staying away from the hot lights? Don't believe it. If I fall, I'll bring the pillars of the temple down with me and pipsqueaks like you will be crushed in the debris.
Paranoia in cranium,
Boris

Dec 10, 2021

Dear Austin, dear Mann,
Why do I not hear you trumpeting from the battlements that I am your trusty leader? You owe every fibre of your ermine cloaks to my efforts. If it wasn't for me, you'd be slouching round Dudley Zoo moaning about gypsies.
Diablo duo,
Boris

Dec 10, 2021

Dear Major,
Your sneering, jeering, leering face is having no effect on
me. You can gather round you all the old grey grandees
you like - Rifkind, Baker et al, but I am the rock of ages,
the Acropolis of Westminister.
Putrescentia in corpus,
Boris

Dec 11, 2021

Dear Rishi,
Ha bloody ha. Your department, bro. Take the rap.
Whited bloody sepulchre Sunak caught in the same
bloody net, eh? That's wiped the wily smirk off your
visage, hasn't it? I go down, you all go down.
Impromptu inebrio,
Boris

Dec 12, 2021

Dear Steve Baker,
You make excellent sense. I hate the whole masking and
jabs tomfoolery too but I'm under pressure from the
damn medicos. Freedom is all. And you voted right on
the Nationality Bill! Send'em back!
Amigo lunatico,
Boris

Dec 13, 2021

Dear Sajid,
I've seen what you're doing. I had HandCock in your post
for good reason: he was useless. As Aristophanes wrote
in 'The Prince': 'The Prince should surround himself with
blinking twerps, so that his star should shine the

brighter.'
Accidenta possibillis,
Boris

Dear Raab,
Remember the words of Circe, 'Say not the noughts availeth the struggle.' Your work in wresting the law from the hands of lefty lawyers and namby-pamby ninnies is exemplary. You're right: the sea is closed.
Dominicus genius prodigius,
Boris

Dear Sajid,
When Caesar stood on the banks of the River Tiger, he knew that time never stands still. You are my trusty steed for when the bugle blows. In the meantime, lay hands on Excalibur to face the Trojan Horse.
Finito interruptus,
Boris

Dear Mogg,
Just heard hapless Shapps blithering on the Today prog. He needs to be holed below the water line ASAP. Tell him it's all over for him and his alter egos. Least we can do afore I go!
Torpedo pronto,
Boris

Dec 15, 2021

Dear Sajid,
So, do I gather or not gather and if I gather do I gather
with the boosted or do I boost before I gather and when I
gather do I gather at a distance when I'm partying or
when I boost?
Clarificatio non clarification,
Boris

Dec 16, 2021

Dear Sajid,
So La France has decided to sever its links with us as if
we are a rotten beam on the 'pont ' over the Tiber.
Caesar knew how to handle the Gauls and so shall I.
Assuming Cassius, Brutus and Rufus haven't stabbed
me by then.
Genitalia laceratio,
Boris

Dec 17, 2021

Dear Mogg,
Tribunes fall by the wayside like chariots on the
Bosphorus. You in your sagacity will stand by your
Churchill. Back to back we'll stave off the Visigoths. Biff,
blam, plop! Yet...yet...a quick get-out would lead to jolly
hols in Mustique, eh?
Fuccuppus exit,
Boris

Dec 17, 2021

Dear Dowden,
You're sounding petulant. I need someone to shore up
the dyke not to blither on about a sea change and noises

off. I do the Shakespeare round here, it's not for a ratty little lieutenant like you to do. I hold the trident, remember.
Persona excrementa,
Boris

Dec 18, 2021

Dear Cressida,
Have got myself in a bit of a fix over this No 10 parties shenanigans. Any chance you could find some trusty Plod to do a quick investigatio and give us all a clean sheet?
Urgentissimus per profundus excrementum,
Boris

Dec 18, 2021

Dear Frost,
You really are a snake. I thought we were like brothers in combat: Mars and Cupid side by side. You were screwing up negotiations over the border with Scotland anyway. Go spend more time with your pension.
Serpentia bastardus,
Boris

Dec 18, 2021

Dear Frost,
Your peremptory memo 'Oven-ready deal, my arse' was gratuitously insulting and disrespectful. You couldn't negotiate your way out of Jupiter's jock strap.
Homo terminus,
Boris

Dec 19, 2021

Dear Rish,
Your jolly in California has gone largely unnoticed,
thanks to media kerfuffles about our Xmas jamborees
and perpetual brown trousers about Covid. Hope you
found some Yankee gold-diggers ready to snaffle up the
NHS.
Avoricius porci,
Boris

Dec 19, 2021

Dear Dominic,
You said a leader should surround himself with idiots so
his own star should sign the brighter. Prob: I'm running
out of idiots. I'm the last clown standing. Probs best to
hire a brain. You free? Reply via Doreen. Carrie reads
these.
Patheticus desperatus,
Boris

Dec 20, 2021

Dear Raab,
You may be a twat but at least you're my twat. I love the
way you go out there and talk total bollocks but it's loyal
bollocks: to the line that the post-prandial bibendum
was 'work'! Shame you can't count tho!
Uno duo quattro,
Boris

Dec 20, 2021

Dear Mogg,
Check this over as a press release:
'I don't have a clear recollection of the work meeting

(and it was a work meeting) in the number 10 garden.
The baby was there, working. Doing a lot of work. All the
time. It's a working baby. And it works.'
Infanta laboris,
Boris

Dec 20, 2021

Dear Mogg,
To tell the blooming truth, if it WAS a work meeting, it's
pretty bloody amazing I was there, eh? I mean how
many Cobra meetings did I miss? Hilarity all round.
Hope the press team can go on massaging this stuff.
Manipulato veritas,
Boris

Dec 20, 2021

Dear Raab,
Terrific that you and the equipage are going on about us
working in 'gruelling conditions', and that we were the
'fulcrum' in the crisis etc etc. It presents us as if we are
intensive care nurses in the furnace of the plague. As if!
Relaxo cabinetto,
Boris

Dec 21, 2021

Dear Raab,
I want you and others to go out there and explain that
the pubs are open - hurrah! - but people shouldn't go in
them - hard cheese! My instructions are clear all the way
to Christmas. Then - well, anything might happen! Tra la!
Confusio terribilissimus,
Boris

Dec 22, 2021

Dear Sajid,
Have you heard? There's a new anti-Covid drug that can help cure Covid, called Paxlovid. Nice bit of Greek there with 'pax'. It means 'white'. Best be careful with this stuff though. Might have to make it available first privately only.
Enterprisus privus gloria,
Boris

Dec 28, 2021

Dear Mogg,
Make sure that no one writes to me or calls me. I've worked my toga off this year and need a break. The pandemic can take a breather while my hand's not on the tiller of state. I'll come back as fit as Fallopian after a bath.
Gluteus maximus in gloria excelsis,
Boris

Dec 29, 2021

Dear Raab,
Got heebyjeebies about Lady Macbeth.The Picts back her, so when she goes for a referendum, they'll support. What's worse, didn't they vote remain? It'd be 2 referenda in 1: leave the UK ,join EU! What about my legacy? The PM who let Scotland go!
Hibernia excrementa,
Boris

Dec 30, 2021
_____

Dear Sajid,
Look busy, do nothing. Love the tents full of empty beds and no staff! And the people love it that they can party. Your job is to slap down the moaners doing vox pops on not being able to buy tests. I can't find my fave Drambuie either.
Saturnalia eternalorum,
Boris

Dec 31, 2021
_____

Dear Mogg,
You're super good on holding the line on behaviour. I've got a New Year worry that the GB public are a tad less respectful these days and the Maxwell case hasn't bloody helped. Can you work up a bit of oratory on respect for Britain's leaders?
Taurus excrementus,
Boris

Dec 31, 2021
_____

Dear Sajid,
We've been very, very clear with the British people: go out, but not too many; get tested, but there aren't enough kits; if you don't know you've got it, maybe you haven't. Now: get some Bolly down me.
Testiculi ad populis britannicus,
Boris

PART IV 2022

A PLETHORA OF CRISES

Evidentia in plentia
(and Boris is leaving 10 Downing Street but not just yet)

'LEVEL UP LIKE A SOCIALIST, BORIS.'

Dear Mogg,
Every time I have to dish out these gongs, my mind drifts towards that moment in the future when I shall claim my honour. What title? Baron Boris sounds bloody good to me. You'll get one too, Moggy: services to being loyal to me.
Nomenclatura dementia,
Boris

Dear Sajid,
What are we doing? Be buggered if I know. I think it's time we did a press co and put up a graph. The GBP love a graph. I could point to it and say, 'We're led by the science.' That's always fun.
Principia mathematica panicattaccica,
Boris

Dear Mogg,
I note the old and new year round-ups are singularly lacking in paeans to me. Could you pen a tribute and lean on media wimps to put it out? 'Utterly trustworthy...tremendously hard-working...great decision-maker...' that sort of stuff.
Inebrio necessitate,
Boris

Dear Sajid,
Cases up, cases down. My head's spinning. What if the cases go down because people can't get hold of the bloomin' tests? Where's that Dido when we need her? I

think we ought to give her another chance. Think of
Cleopatra and the geese.
Equestriana heroica,
Boris

Jan 7, 2022

Dear Brownlow,
V. sozz, had to spill beans on Great Exhib proj. We had a
good thing going: you pay for refurb, i get you audience
with Oliver Dowdy, you top up party coffers. Now Ange,
the single parent is all over it. We'll get through this,
amigo!
Lucre et lucre et lucre,
Boris

Jan 9, 2022

Dear Sajid,
I think we've bloomin' well cracked it: the infection rates
go up or down depending on how often people test. All
we have to do is test less and restrict the number of test
kits out there and infection rate goes down. Seneca
defeats Sparta.
Bogus statisticus,
Boris

Jan 10, 2022

Dear Gove,
Am talking with others about how they might take it in
turns to truffle round studios floating the idea of cutting
isolation times down to about 4 hours. At the end of the
day, people have just got to accept that loved ones are
going to cop it.
Non mea problemmo,
Boris

Jan 10, 2022

Dear Mogg,
The fact is that I can't deny that I would have denied that I had denied I was at the party. I could have denied that I might have denied that the party was a party. At the moment, I'm denying that I'm not denying.
Veritas impossibillus,
Boris

Jan 11, 2022

Dear Sajid,
I need you to get out there and save my bacon, if you'll excuse the expression. Talk about vaccinations, boosters, levelling up, northern powerhouse - anything. How about Starmer can't find his underpants? I know mine are in a terrible state.
Sub toga desperandum,
Boris

Jan 11, 2022

Dear Gove,
What do you mean my days are numbered? Shut your whiny cake hole, Gove. You got thrown out of the rugger team for crying because your shorts were muddy. Your plots come to nothing. You: less Cassius, more sissy.
Hospitalitus superbus ad Via Downinnius,
Boris

Jan 11, 2022

Dear Rache,
I've got to hide till PMQ tomozz. You've got that cellar, right?. I can get an unmarked security van to park outside your door. I'm wearing a black wig and grey

beard. I'll text you as I arrive, you have the door open and
I'll leap in.
In extremis absurdus,
Boris

Jan 11, 2022

Dear Mogg,
I need everyone who was at the bash to say they didn't
see me there. Each of them has to come up with a
plausible cock and bull story: bad eyes, drunk, left early,
allergic to nuts - anything. As did Socrates and the
Sabine Women.
Alibi multiplificatio,
Boris

Jan 12, 2022

Dear Mogg,
How's about that?! I did a grovel without taking the rap.
More slippery than Neptune in the Cloaca Maxima. I
gather there are a few odds and sods blubbing on about
not being able to say goodbye. Not my fault. No hanging
offence, amigos.
Ego grandissimus,
Boris

Jan 12, 2022

Dear Sue Gray,
I haven't written this memo. Please delete it the moment
you've read it. A lot hangs on your enquiry, including my
neck. I respect your independence but you will
appreciate that your post can be restructured at any
time.
Venomus in fusilli,
Boris

Jan 13, 2022

Dear Mogg,
Much appreciated slavish backing you gave me on
Newsnight. Teensy bit bothered by your calling leader of
the Scotty botty Tories 'lightweight'. We're trying to keep
the troops together backing their centurion: remember
Augustus versus Sparta.
Mutini insomnia,
Boris

Jan 14, 2022

Dear Truss,
Excellent work with the 'We now need to move on' line.
Glorious psychobabble that'll go down well with the
woke-gone-mad Guardianistas, I'm sure.
Psycho excremento,
Boris

Jan 14, 2022

Dear staff,
Your behaviour during the lockdowns was reprehensible
and unforgivable. You should take your guidance from
me. I am the touchstone on how to behave in
appropriate ways both on a personal and political level.
Heads will roll.
Executio necessitatus,
Boris

Jan 14, 2022

Dear Dominic,
I know you're the leaker. You were at the same parties that you're bloomin' shunting through to the media snake-pit. As you pull me down you'll pull the castle on top of you, just as Romulus did to Cleopatra.
Patella in nando,
Boris

Jan 15, 2022

Dear staff,
So you lot are feeling miffed by my 'apology' in the House. O boo hoo. Face it, you're very low down in the food chain. I'm not going to go out there and say your jollies were down to me. When it's my neck or yours, it's yours every time.
Fiasco al fresco,
Boris

Jan 16, 2022

Dear Nadine,
Good to see your plans to give the BBC a kicking. I thought of Herodotus pinning Hannibal to the Golden Fleece. Nation shall speak unto nation but not via Broadcasting House, eh babe?
Repressio pressio,
Boris

Novak Djokovic was not able to play in the Australian Open 2022 tennis tournament because he refused to be vaccinated. Unvaccinated people were not allowed into Australia unless they had a specific medical reason. He thought that the Australian government would grant him an exception to the ruling.

Jan 16, 2022

Dear Djokovic,
You're manna from heaven, a gift from the gods. Your every move (or non-move hah!) is reported on every news outlet here thus pushing my perceived misdemeanours down the menu. Huzza! Can you say you're not getting jabbed every day?
Novac no visa gratis gratis,
Boris

Jan 17, 2022

Dear Zahawi,
Thanks as ever for your superb backing in the face of the tyrant Nick Robinson. I particularly loved you saying that I got all the calls right on the pandemic. Hah! I wasn't even at the meetings in the beginning, but no one knows about that.
In absentia gloria,
Boris

Jan 19, 2022

Dear Rishi,
I hope you were listening to Today: me being lauded as the great leader with the weight of state on my shoulders, too busy to have twigged it was a party. Be like him, young man, and not like Virgil suckling the wolf.
Omnibus terminus,
Boris

Jan 19, 2022

Dear Nadine,
Murdoch's dumped me. I used to be the solution to the problem. Now I'm just the problem. All his outlets are

raining Big Jobs on me. Do you know that model he married? Can we lean on her just as Pontius Pilate leant on Nero?
Cloaca australiae,
Boris

MP for Bury South, Christian Wakeford crossed the floor of the House to join Labour seats. He had been dissatisfied since the Owen Patterson trouble.

Jan 19, 2022

Dear Christian Wakeford,
Words cannot express how low you have stooped. Joining Labour and the Marxists? Only men of exceedingly poor character betray their leader, their party and their country as you have and as Neptune betrayed Vesuvius.
Serpentas serpentatis,
Boris

Jan 19, 2022

Dear Mogg,
Who does Davies think he is? He's just a jumped up Cockney boy trying to sound like Cicero. No Sword of Hercules poised above me, Moggo! I am deeply grateful for your loyalty. You are loyal, aren't you? Aren't you? Await your reply.
Nil,
Boris

Jan 19, 2022

Dear Sajid,
I'm very much enjoying the story that I'm responsible for the success of the vaccination programme. I see myself has having invented it, distributed it and injecting people with it. Crumb of comfort for me as erstwhile friends ambush and persecute me.
Ego,
Boris

Jan 19, 2022

Dear Sajid,
I see your plan to turn hospitals into academies is coming on apace. This makes it easy for academies to compete with each other which will finally enable us to regard patients as cheap or expensive: avoid the expensive ones - very ill, yuk!
Profitorum primo,
Boris

Jan 20, 2022

Dear Mogg,
I'm out of the woods! Again I spring free. 'Pugnacious' was how my HoC performance yesterday was described by Laura of K. The rebels have retreated, slunk back to their caves. I am Achilles without the dodgy heel.
Impermeabillissimus rex,
Boris

Jan 20, 2022

Dear Mogg,
Have you seen the latest from the Oily Wragg? He says our Whips blackmail backbenchers! Hah! If only we did.

In fact, some of his claims about threatening MPs with withdrawal of public funds from their constituencies sound rather good.
Mafia in casa,
Boris

Jan 28, 2022

Dear Mogg,
You've batted for me heroically so far but what I'll need from you is some dexterous footwork. We'll need to make the 'Report' look 'open to interpretation' - 50 shades of Gray, as Socrates said to Cleopatra.
Pro ego pro bono,
Boris

Jan 28, 2022

Dear Mogg,
Religion is your department: is it possible to have the fragrant Cressida beatified? Never in the history of human conquest has so much been done by so few for so few: phew! The Gray Report will end up being shorter than veni vidi vici.
In toto zero,
Boris

Jan 29, 2022

Dear Truss,
I need you to ramp up the Russian threat even more. I'll be strutting my stuff on the Eastern Front and expect some Napoleonic long shots of Le Johnson in the snow written up in Ciceronian prose by my press amigos.
Hyperbole testiculatorum,
Boris

Jan 29, 2022

Dear Rishi,
You need to sit on the stories about London being
awash with roubles. The theme song we're singing is
the big bear in the east so oligarch lolly finding its way
into our party coffers is counterproductive. Squash it.
Financio obscuro,
Boris

**An investigation into allegations of lockdown-breaching parties
inside Downing Street was ordered in December by the government. Sue Gray, a senior civil servant was asked to be responsible for a report. The public were very keen to know the
findings of the Sue Gray report.**

Jan 29, 2022

Dear Mogg,
Am poring over Gray's Elegy as you read this. Usual
woke BS about people's feelings (yawn). Why do the
metropolitan north London elite emote so much? Re
Gray: worry not. Nothing there to lever limpet Johnson
from the rock of ages.
Nausea ad absurdum,
Boris

Jan 30, 2022

Dear Azurri,
I see you've handed over some documents that relate to
that thing we had years ago when I was Mayor. Big
mistake. You've forgotten that I am more slippery than
Poseidon in the Sargasso Sea when Augustus Caesar
tried to spear him with a trident.
Ego eternus,
Boris

Jan 30, 2022

Dear Truss,
Tell the Ukrainians to pipe down about telling us not to
'panic' that the Ruskies are amassing their forces in
more numbers than Caesar gathered for the
Peloponnesian War. We're Brexit Britain flexing our
world-beating muscles on the world stage.
Leo brittannicus,
Boris

Jan 30, 2022

Dear Mogg,
Marvellous how you're all sticking to the script: 'Boris
got all the big calls right'! Hah! The comedic truth is I
didn't even know what the calls were, let alone get them
right. You know that, I know that, but out there Rome
doth not know.
Veritas obscuro,
Boris

Jan 31, 2022

Dear Gove,
Your line about Christian forgiveness is especially
welcome: it hits just the right tone of holier-than-thou
mixed with gaslighting. You're getting better at this
game. Presumably you're after my job.
Garbagio interminablio,
Boris

Jan 31, 2022

Dear Mogg,
What I want from the team is one helluva lot of
busywork: lots of lovely brexitty stuff, tax stuff, war stuff,
levelling uppy stuff and of course jubilee stuff. Sue
Gray's Elegy will fade from view like the bear that
Romulus suckled.
Parlio per mea cloaca,
Boris

Jan 31, 2022

Dear Cressida,
A quick peruse of the Lady Jane Gray's Elegy tells me
that your spanner was not merely put in the works but
biffed it full and square on its head. Sue G. could hardly
squeak for fear of rattling the thin blue line. Well done,
Dame Cressy.
Corruptio ubiquitus,
Boris

Jan 31, 2022

Dear Mogg,
Put out a statement from me later, as follows: 'It is not
possible for me to comment on the hypothetical
question of whether I was at the party in my flat
because I do not know if I was there or not. We must
wait for the police report."
Deceptus magnificat,
Boris

Feb 1, 2022

Dear Mogg,
I wake this morn with a spring in my step. Hah! I beat off
the catcallers in the Commons. I am Horatio on the

bridge over the Bosphorus fending off the Visigoths.
Don't tell anyone I said this: the parties were bloomin'
great.
Excrementa confidentialis,
Boris

Feb 1, 2022

Dear Truss,
As you know I am making a major intervention in world
diplomacy by heading to Ukraine. Watch and learn. You
will see how I play Russia for fools, winding them round
my little e finger just as Odysseus bewitched Circe.
Colossus tossus,
Boris

Feb 1, 2022

Dear Mogg,
I'm busy keeping the Ruskies at bay on the eastern front
like Caesar holding out against Sparta. You'll have to
deal with the ABBA question. In case you don't know,
they were a Norwegian band. Carrie was playing them
the night Cummings died.
Ego in excremento,
Boris

Feb 2, 2022

Dear Gove,
Your skill at proliferating meaningless blather is much
needed today. You and I know that levelling up means
nothing minus zero but you've got to pretend otherwise
as you tour the studios talking cock. You're just the man
for that.
Agenda testiculorum,
Boris

Feb 2, 2022

Dear Mogg,
Some oiks in the Lower Fourth are calling on me to
resign. Their poor little squeamish souls object to my
fiendish stab at the whey-faced Starmer in the House. If
they can't stand the heat, get out of the garden party.
Descendem ad detritus,
Boris

Feb 3, 2022

Dear Sajid,
The project for Feb is Covid Over. I need you to strain
every sinew to keep death counts off the front pages
and exert pressure to divert the dreary Long Covid lobby.
Your delivery-focussed PM has slain the Pandemic just
as Achilles slew Nero.
Deceptio ineptio,
Boris

Feb 3, 2022

Dear Rishi,
Remember, if people are poor it's because they are
either feckless or useless. We can stuff quids in their
mouths but they only spend it on drugs and booze. But
in the woke world we live in, we have to keep a lid on this
way of thinking.
Impecunia idioticus,
Boris

Feb 3, 2022

Dear Mogg,
The midgets are quitting: mean-minded munchkins with
narry a smidgeon of decency about them. Political

advisors? Hah! Whatever they advised I did the opposite.
I lead: they leave.
Solo in pogo,
Boris

Dear Mogg,
When Hannibal defeated Vesuvius, was that the end?
No. Vesuvius struck back and prevailed. We must learn
from the past in order to make the mistakes of the
future. Number 10 is full of maggots.
Quis quo quit,
Boris

Dear Gibb,
For years you've promoted our superb policies of
academies, free schools and phonics, but today you sink
to the depths of Elysium. You have jeopardised this
great government on account of a bit of cake. History
will forget you.
Peptic apoplectic,
Boris

Dear Nadine,
How marvellous to hear your silken tones on the Today
programme. Your tribute to me was greater than
Aristophanes' peroration in the Forum. I love your
appreciation of my focus on delivery. Mind you, isn't that
what PMs are supposed to do?
Sycophanta madonna,
Boris

Dear Mogg,
When the Rolling Stones sang 'I am the walrus' little did they know that ringing round my head on this sylvan Saturday would be the words, 'I am the limpet'. No commentator's knife will ever lever me off the rock of destiny.
Donna immobile in vitro,
Boris

Dear Sajid,
Am listening to BBC Any Questions. Delighted to hear that I'm responsible for the vaccine. My first skill is of course Classical Literature but unbeknownst to me (prior to the Pandemic) is my world-beating knowledge of medical science.
Bacteria in cerebellum,
Boris

Dear Connor Burns,
Your loyalty is eye-watering. I will be forever grateful to you. Should I be in a position in the future to reward you for your kindness, I will repay your devotion just as Julius Caesar was able to repay Brutus.
Ultima ultima tempus,
Boris

Dear Kwasi,
Good to see you turning up for me today. Voluntarily, or was your arm twisted? Glad you used the word 'reset'.

Sounds like 'advance' but means absolutely nothing.
Please don't refer to manifesto promises again though.
Tantrum in pesto,
Boris

Feb 7, 2022

Dear Nadine,
Why are you in Saudi Arabia? Who sent you there? I need
my Praetorian Guard right here being praetorian. At any
moment one of the backstabbers could come in here
and hand me the Black Spot, just as Odysseus handed
one to Caesar.
Panic titanic,
Boris

Feb 7, 2022

Dear Guto,
I just heard you telling the world that I sang the great
Whitney Houston hit 'I will survive' when I met you. Easy
does it, amigo. That sort of thing is confidential. As for
you saying that I'm not 'completely' a clown. Au
contraire: I am.
Quid pro quo yoyo,
Boris

Feb 7, 2022

Dear Guto,
I chose you because I have great admiration for the
Scots. I've got a sticky patch coming up and no one
wants to get stuck in a sticky patch, och aye. I'll need
you to navigate me past the Scylla and Chlamydia of the
Gray and Met reports.
Caledonia fidelis,
Boris

Feb 7, 2022

Dear Truss,
We've been bloomin' upstaged by the little Frenchyman.
Who does he think he is? Napoleon? And we know what
happened to Napoleon en route to Leningrad! I'll see
what my noble Scotsman Guto can do for me.
Sello tapio,
Boris

Feb 8, 2022

Dear Truss,
Hope you picked up on my phraseology: 'We will not
flinch' over Ukraine, 'we will remain unmoveable'? Don't
worry that no one's asking us to flinch or move, it just
sounds good. The lion roars. As did the Cylops when he
ate Virgil.
Opus pocus,
Boris

Feb 8, 2022

Dear Mogg,
Did Aristotle apologise to Nero? Did Theseus apologise
to Catullus? No. No more will I. I am above and beyond
apologies. They are the stuff of lesser men than I. The
world spins on its sixpence. The sun carries the moon in
its cake-tin.
Crisis terminus,
Boris

Feb 8, 2022

Dear Mogg,
So you're in charge of all the lovely Brexitty stuff! I
remember you talking during the Referendum run-up

about how ordinary people would pay less for their 'footwear'. That sort of thing went down very well with ordinary people.
Condescensio ad plebs,
Boris

Feb 8, 2022

Dear Cabinet,
Hercules Boris has cleared out the Gordian Stables. All is refreshed and reset. I'm ramping up my sleeves, getting all the big calls oven-ready, my toecaps over the line. Adrian's Wall wasn't built in a day but Rome was.
Vindolanda panda,
Boris

Feb 9, 2022

Dear Truss,
Macron? Micron more like. Putin has chewed up Monsieur le Président and spat out the bones just as the wolf ate poor Romulus. The law of diplomacy: where the lion roars, the cockerel grovels.
Vivat tapioca,
Boris

Feb 9, 2022

Dear Nadine,
Reports coming to me that BBC Red-io 4 did a 'More or Less' job on my stats about unemployment and crime. Please remind the pinkos there that I'm PM: I say what I want. Some days the sun goes round the earth. Or round me.
Orbito ergo sum,
Boris

Feb 9, 2022

Dear Cressida,
The nation and I would be most obliged if you could be exceedingly diligent in your work on the matter of parties at Number 10. Ideally, it should take at least 2 years to complete.
Memo obligato destructus,
Boris

Feb 9, 2022

Dear Mogg,
A photo is circulating of me, man with a wreath round his neck and pixelated image of a woman. Also in the picture is an open bottle of a bloomin' good champagne. I suggest we talk to Priti to do what she can to remove it.
Excremento et excremento et excremento,
Boris

Feb 9, 2022

Dear Mogg,
Put out a statement quick that this was an international trade meeting for the garment industry. I was demonstrating a tie.
Taurus excrementum pronto,
Boris

Metropolitan Police announced they were to review their decision not to investigate a No. 10 quiz party after a leaked photo of Boris Johnson in attendance surfaced.

Feb 9, 2022

Dear Cressida,
You haven't seen this pic. Your gaze was averted by crime statistics, the need to clean up the Met, your irritation with Sadiq Khan, security at London Zoo, issues with street lighting in Kensington - anything!
Camera obscura,
Boris

Feb 9, 2022

Dear Mogg,
Who's this Pippa Crerar figure who's splashed the Xmas quiz? Get digging. Who are her parents? Past liaisons? Check out who's she's besmirched before. Fight fire with fire or we sink in the briny and the sea god Mars takes us.
Canelloni desperatus,
Boris

Feb 9, 2022

Dear Sajid,
The big question you need to answer is: are the right people dying? If they are mostly old, poor and disabled then we're in the clear. Masks off, open the gates. I'll be crowned Prince of Fun and Freedom.
Et tutu Brute,
Boris

Feb 10, 2022

Dear Major, (in truth, Minor, surely)
Your sniping from the sidelines will fail. You forget that in contrast to you, I am the Colossus of Rome, guarding the harbour, visible from afar. Your barely disguised call to my men to mutiny will fall on deaf eyes.
Con funghi,
Boris

Feb 10, 2022

Dear Cressida,
As you'll know from the great epic, Thesaurus and Cressida, all is not lost till it's lost. What you didn't see, you spoke not of; the can you saw, you kicked down the

Via Appia, for which we'll be ever grateful.
Carnivalis ad villa numero dix invisibilis,
Boris

Feb 11, 2022

Dear Mogg,
They may depart, but Boris stays. I am the steadfast
Parthenon to the onward rush of the Tiber. I am the
bearer of joyous news: masks off, tests stop. If people
drop dead, it's their fault - coolio! History will slaver me
with kisses.
Dido in mango,
Boris

Feb 12, 2022

Dear Mogg,
Have you heard about the questionnaire? The Met have
sent each of us one to self-declare whether we are or
ever have been a member of the Number 10 Party. I've
said no before; no reason I can't do it again, as Sisyphus
said to the Minotaur.
Illicito panto,
Boris

Feb 14, 2022

Dear Mogg,
Tbh even a little war could save my skin, let alone a
bloomin' great conflagration. I must say it's terrific fun
getting a glimpse into MoD's War Room. Churchill or
what! Fetch me a siren suit, Moggy and I'll be in this job
for years.
Tornado in rectum,
Boris

The Rusian military was carrying out large-scale military exercises with the Belarus army near the borders of Ukraine. This was causing a great deal of speculation across the world.

Feb 16, 2022

Dear Mogg,
I think we're still on for a skirmish in Ukraine which is good news for me. If I could get that Blair-Bush optic, standing on an airfield, my hair looking tousled and endearing...it would win me more support than Jason got from the Cyclops.
Pro patria cornetto,
Boris

Feb 17, 2022

Dear Mogg,
Damn good news about this Storm Eustace. After it's all over, I can be ferried about in a high viz jacket and helmet looking active and sympathetic. People in distress love me turning up on their doorsteps being hearty.
Catastrophe pro bono,
Boris

Feb 18, 2022

Dear Zahawi,
Nice one. You've put your foot down and told all those Trot teachers to stint their clap. The woke are up in arms because you've cut them off at the pass just as Persephone intercepted Hannibal in the Pyrenees.
Gluteus maximus in tesco,
Boris

Feb 19, 2022

Dear Mogg,
Filled in their bloomin' questionnaire. No room on the
form for my full name though. Under, what was your
reason for being there blah di blah? I wrote, 'To lead the
country just as Catullus led his.' Does the Met give
questionnaires to all suspects?
Nemesis conga,
Boris

Feb 19, 2022

Dear Mogg,
Every time I speak it's as if Winston is in me. I think the
Woke call it 'channelling' - but for me, it's more that I
inherit the mantle. I blossom in the sun of his greatness,
don't you think? Mind you, he was Harrow. You and I are
not.
Semper hyperbole,
Boris

Feb 19, 2022

Dear Mogg,
It's at times like these, I wish we had conscription. How
lucky were they, those PMs who could turn out in front
of the serried ranks of thousands urging them on to
great deeds in the Crimea or on the Somme - then
consoling the widows back in Blighty.
Magnus Boris

Feb 19, 2022

Dear Mogg,
Every word I speak on the world stage is a nail in the
muffin of those who would crucify me for a few minutes
of fun in the garden. O Cerberus, thou wert ever the cat
in sylvan seas aloft. The putative rebels fade like the
Wooden Horse in Rome.
Grissini fidelis,
Boris

Feb 20, 2022

Dear Mogg,
Maddening: micro Macron has been parleying with Putin
for bloomin' hours. Like as not, he'll secure some
settlement leaving me looking like second fiddle and
Britain paddling along behind La France! Can we
sabotage him?
Cumulus animus pus,
Boris

Feb 21, 2022

Dear Mogg,
Spread the word: I am the bearer of great gifts: the right
of every true born Englishman - freedom. Thanks to my
pioneer work as the great vaccinator, today I release the
population from its shackles just as Perseus released
Medusa from hers.
Testiculi mendacius,
Boris

Feb 21, 2022

Dear Mogg,
If my old pal Putin pulls back from the brink, I need you

to concoct a tale of how it's all thanks to me. I was thinking of something along the lines of the Colossus of Roads halts the Bear in its tracks.
Epic perjurio,
Boris

Feb 21, 2022

Dear Sajid,
Can you confirm that you are holding Chris Whitty and Patrick Valance in the cellars under Trafalgar Square? Thing is, I may have to answer something about this in PMQs and I need to know the truth in order to avoid it.
Veritas in anus,
Boris

Feb 22, 2022

Dear Mogg,
Am concerned with everyone throwing around the word 'oligarch' as if they are the big bad wolf. If we take it too far, people might think our great entrepreneurs, Branson and the like are oligarchs too. Then we'll be in real trouble, eh?
Croesus Britannicus,
Boris

Feb 23, 2022

Dear Mogg,
Ideal scenario is for Putin to come to a standstill so I can take credit for stopping him in his tracks just as Cleopatra halted the Minotaur. I need some cred to stop the mouths of the backbench mob.
Colon desperandum,
Boris

On February 24th, Putin authorised 'Special Military Operations' in Ukraine. It was announced on Russian television. Russian missiles began a bombardment of Ukrainian cities, including the capital Kyiv.

Feb 26, 2022

Dear Lebedev,
Best if you lie low for a bit. Ah - 'lie low' doesn't mean tell low lies, which we don't do - ah! I'll rephrase that: cavey! That's Latin. Sort of. Ah. Anyway - ah - you get the point.
Sotto voce vice,
Boris

Mar 8, 2022

Dear Priti,
You're doing a fantastic job with this refugee stuff. Am loving the way you say things that we aren't doing and leading people to believe that it's what we are doing. It really annoys the woke wolves at your gate. Keep it up.
Cataclysmo euphoria,
Boris

Mar 9, 2022

Dear Shapps,
Love it when HQ send you out to face the Today team. Your chirpy blather is like froth on Socrates' beer before the invasion of Britain. Verily, we are not trying to bring in refugees, we're trying to keep them out. Ever onwards.
Ars longa vita brexit,
Boris

Mar 10, 2022

Dear Priti,
This whole visas thing is getting out of hand. The

principle is that a) we love the Ukrainians b) we want everyone to know that we love the Ukrainians c) we don't want them here.

You are the only person I know who can juggle this one.

Carpe diet,

Boris

Mar 16, 2022

Dear Gove,

Your purple-faced outrage was marvellous. Let's hope it masks the fact that we've created this big puff about an open door by telling people that they can host a Ukrainian but slammed it shut by saying they've got to know one first!

Prestidigitationis testiculi,

Boris

Nazanin Zaghari-Ratcliffe visited her parents in Iran in 2016 with her one-year-old daughter. She was arrested in Iran's capital and was accused of plotting against the Iranian government. At the time Boris Johnson was Foreign Secretary in Theresa May's government.

Mar 16, 2022

Dear Mogg,

We need to tie down the hacks and stop them blaming me for the Zaghari-Ratcliffe stuff. Could you cobble something together about 'delicate balance', 'guided by Intelligence'? And I'm the hero who's saved her, just as Plato saved Hadrian.

Samosa in toto,

Boris

Mar 18, 2022

Dear Mogg,
Am disappointed that praise for me for solving the
Iranian wotsit has been rather muted. I cut the Guardian
Knot just as Nero cut loose the Golden Fleece and yet
the sneerers want to blame me for it taking so long!
Ego et bacon,
Boris

Mar 22, 2022

Dear Mogg,
Glad someone put that story out that I'm desperate to
get to Ukraine. Makes me seem like a thwarted hero.
(See Theseus before he slew Mark Antony.) Partygate is
just a distant mirage blown by the arms of yore into the
sands of fate.
Hocus pocus locus,
Boris

Mar 26, 2022

Dear Raab,
Great stuff you're doing on banning wokery. This is a
country as free as Rome where a slave could travel
freely in service of his master. If we do nothing else, we
will weevil out the wokes, won't we?
Libertas upmias,
Boris

Mar 27, 2022

Dear Rishi,
Very sorry to see that you got some adverse press
following your budget thingy. You were teflon up till then,
weren't you? The whingers think you've been tough on

the poor. Has to be done, though.
Carry on.
Placebo wasabi,
Boris

Mar 28, 2022

Dear Zahawi,
Genius move with this English and Maths wotsit. We're
telling teachers to wake up, and tell parents if their
children need to do better. Why hasn't anyone ever
thought of this before? We're like Cassandra warning
Caesar about the Ides of April.
Fresco in tesco,
Boris

Mar 28, 2022

Dear Zahawi,
This stuff about teaching kids the 'benefits of the British
Empire' is terrific. We could make it compulsory that kids
dress up as slaves and sing 'De Camptown Races'. Keep
the ideas coming, Z.!
Super patio,
Boris

Mar 30, 2022

Dear Mogg,
So far so good on the Lockdown Party thingy. The point
is I'm the helmsman at the pinnacle steering the ship of
fate away from the rocks of despond. I am Oedipus in
the Odyssey. In short, do what you can to keep the story
off the front pages.
Bona fido bona canis,
Boris

Mar 30, 2022

Dear Mogg,
Outrageous stuff that Starmer comes out with. I'm beginning to think that we need to hold him to account. Perhaps with some kind of Truth Tsar. Perhaps Shapps could step up and be Fact Checker in Chief. Like Pandora's Fox.
Scrotum totem,
Boris

Mar 30, 2022

Dear Mogg,
What the bullying ninnies don't realise is that if they succeed in getting rid of me, they get something worse! Hah bloody hah! It's just the same as when Caligula handed power over to Pontius Pilate.
Rictus circus,
Boris

Apr 4, 2022

Dear Mogg,
I'm putting out the line that I didn't lie, I was misinformed. Fair enough because I frequently misinform myself. The sands of destiny close over the morass of unwanted winds.
Testiculi in cranium,
Boris

Apr 7, 2022

Dear Kwasi,
Love your style: bumbling along, talking boloney but coming over as unflappable as Cassandra on the cross with Spartacus. None of these interviewers land a blow,

anyway!
Fandango corruptango,
Boris

Apr 8, 2022

Dear Rishi,
Best approach: just laugh it off. It's always worked for
me. Remember: you're not responsible for your wife's
actions. You are not your wife's keeper (even if you are
hers - ha!) It all went well for Midas, eh?
Porcus porcissimus,
Boris

**Boris Johnson visited the capital of Ukraine on the 9th April. He
toured the bomb scarred streets with the President Volodymr
Zelenskiy and pledged that Britain would supply armoured
vehicles and missiles.**

Apr 10, 2022

Dear Mogg,
Did you see me?! Striding down the street with the
Zominsky chap. I was Alexander on the day he defeated
Hannibal. And did you hear me on about lions and roars
and stuff? If that doesn't wipe out the memory of Party-
bloody-gate, nothing will.
Oratorio testiculo,
Boris

**The French presidential election was held on the 10th and 24th
April. No candidate won a majority in the first round. In the
runoff Emmanuel Macron beat Marine Le Pen.**

Apr 10, 2022

Dear Mogg,
We need to prepare some flannel in case Martine Le Pen
wins. Le Pen is mightier than the sword, perhaps? Good
to see little Micron get a pasting and we need a unity of
right-minded right-wingers with me at its head like the
Colossus of Roads.
Fascisti pizzeria,
Boris

Apr 12, 2022

Dear Rishi,
I'm guessing you and/or missus can afford the fine but
to tell the truth I'm a bit strapped. Any chance of tiding
me over till I've got the readies myself. I'm as broke as
Croesus.
Impecunius inebrius,
Boris

Apr 12, 2022

Dear Mogg,
All clear! Full steam ahead! Tally ho! Even as Horatio
struck down the Persians, so does Boris lay waste to the
doubters and lily-livered gremlins. I will stay in office like
the barnacle sticks to a ship's bottom.
Ego ego ego,
Boris

Apr 13, 2022

Dear Mogg,
What is truth? I think we need to go to the British people
with a modern definition, fit for purpose for today's
world. We've lapsed into a rigid, top-down, quasi-

Stalinist view that truth is about being true. We need something more flexible.
Veritas upmias,
Boris

Apr 13, 2022

Dear Raab,
Do we need a ministerial code? No. Put out the statement: The British people entrusted me to do things and they've been done. Oh, better rephrase that, in case people think I'm saying that it's the British people who were done.
Crisis cranium,
Boris

Apr 13, 2022

Dear Raab,
Can you get out a government statement along the lines of 'Perjury is good'? Too many judges and lawyers stick unthinkingly to the idea that they are upholders of the truth. Priti's attack on 'lefty lawyers' was a good start.
Vomitarium aquarium,
Boris

Apr 13, 2022

Dear Carrie,
They're probs going to hit me and you with some more fines. Any chance you could come up with a line about the brat running off into the garden and us chasing him? Needs must etc. (Btw, was it Bolly or Moet?)
Carnivali ad inferno,
Boris

Apr 13, 2022

Dear Mogg,
I submitted my resignation earlier today. I handed it in to
the Prime Minister but I heard just now that he's not
accepted it.
Conundrum testiculi,
Boris

Apr 13, 2022

Dear Carrie,
Are we agreed that the vermin Cummings is behind our
present travails? It is he, surely, who has leaked the leaks
in order to divert our attention from his own
misdemeanours just as Leda hid the swan from Mark
Antony.
Procul harem opus no 23,
Boris

Apr 13, 2022

Dear Mogg,
Do you remember that absolute darling of a woman who
used to work with that Pesto fellow, and then worked for
me? Why was it that she resigned? Something tells me it
was for laughing? Whatever it was, am glad that
principles were involved.
Allegra pellagra,
Boris

Apr 13, 2022

Dear Mogg,
When the Gray Report rains its lead weight of the
Guardian Knot of Damocles on our sword, then might
we find ourselves neck-deep in the merde. For we must

be as prepared as the Parthenon in the face of Vesuvius, Moggy.
Testes strangulatis,
Boris

Apr 13, 2022

Dear Edwina,
Not unoblivious to your charms as I am, I could not have been more overwhelmed than by the generosity of your comments on today's media outlets. You really are a queen of quips, a princess of primetime TV.
Salmonella pestilentia,
Boris

Apr 13, 2022

Dear Carrie,
I see myself as the hero in a great classical tragedy, along the lines of one written by Catullus. Traditionally, darling, the hero has a fatal flaw. The only problem for the playwright writing one about me is that I don't have a fatal flaw.
Homer eroticus,
Boris

Priti Patel, the home secretary enacted her policy of sending illegal immigrants to Rawanda having signed an agreement with the Rawandan foreign minister.

Apr 14, 2022

Dear Priti,
Great plan for refugees and Rwanda! (Remind me, where
is Rwanda?) I thought the old 'hulks' idea was good too.
I loved that bit in 'Great Expectations' where we get a
glimpse of the shackles the prisoners wore but Rwanda
is certainly sunnier.
Custodies cruellia,
Boris

Apr 14, 2022

Dear Carrie,
The media keep talking about more Partygate parties
coming down the line. Do you remember these? To tell
the truth, I think I must have been blotto because I don't
recall them at all. Good defence! Worked for Reagan!
Comatose vino rose,
Boris

Apr 14, 2022

Dear Mogg,
Hark how my noble troops stand by their leader! Lo how
the mean-spirited media struggle to find the disloyal!
Was there ever a praetorian guard so praetorian? We will
ignore the treachery of Lord Nobody who has jumped
ship like Icarus from the moon.
Vas deferens,
Boris

Apr 14, 2022

Dear Zahawi,
I thought that your words on 'behaviour' in schools were
terrific. We really do have to go hard on bad behaviour

wherever it happens. Bad behaviour in schools leads to bad behaviour in adults and look where that get us, eh? How's the stable?
Tibia et fibula,
Boris

Dear Sajid,
Your main job right now is to hide. Basically, we are saying Covid is over because I cured it. You appearing in public reminds the public that people are dying, which is off-message. Have you thought of Rwanda?
Photosynthesis in circus,
Boris

Dear Mogg,
We've got them talking about deporting these immigrant people to Rwanda. Remind me, didn't some pretty horrid stuff happen there a few years ago? Anyway, people getting racked up about Rwanda is better than them being pissed off with Partygate.
Audio excrementum,
Boris

Dear Priti,
Did you see Andrew Peirce on the Paper Review last night? He was really rooting for our boats to Rwanda. My worry is what happens if they won't get on board. What do we need? Tasers? Whips? Cattle prods? Do they need to be chained?
Inhumanitatis necessitatis,
Boris

Apr 14, 2022

Dear Priti,
It may prove difficult to identify all these people we're
shipping to Rwanda. Their names may be very foreign
so we should look into numbering them, and using some
kind of tattoo system.
Immoralis bona est,
Boris

Apr 15, 2022

Dear Mogg,
As we approach this holiest of times in the calendar, my
thoughts turn to the great principles laid down 2000
years ago: compassion, truth and love for our fellow
humans. I think people see me as a standard bearer for
these values.
Lingo garbagio,
Boris

Apr 16, 2022

Dear Priti,
Let not the words of the naysayers impede your
mission. The sands of Rwanda will wash away the
champagne corks of Partygate. Btw, when you've done a
costing, can you bury it in an addendum just as Caesar
buried Mark Antony?
Transportio concentratio,
Boris

Apr 17, 2022

Dear Mogg,
Canterbury is telling us we're being ungodly! We don't
have to take any notice of what that Welby fellow says. I
mean, you kick with the other leg, and think he's some

kind of heretical upstart, eh? The Pontiff likes Rwanda, just as Nero loved Sparta.
Blotto voce,
Boris

Apr 17, 2022

Dear Priti,
I fear the Rwanda ploy has flopped. We need some more red meat to fling at the dogs. I suggest troops on Dover Beach. And a frigate. History tells us a sea-battle was what sunk Hannibal. Hoist the flag, and sink the dinghies, Priti!
Jingo lingo,
Boris

Apr 18, 2022

Dear Carrie,
When I resign, we need to make a dignified retreat. Like me presenting a TV series: a trek round the Roman Empire: 'Boris Goes Roamin' with the Romans'. Or a follow-up to Attenborough but more about me: 'Boris Saves the Planet'.
Orbis in rectum,
Boris

Apr 18, 2022

Dear Mogg,
What is truth? Was I put on earth to be the great arbiter of right and wrong or am I here to get things done? I walk in the steps of Alexander the Great not Mother Teresa. I stride the streets of Kviv and Lyiv like Circe in Carthage.
Colostrum pro rata,
Boris

Apr 18, 2022

Dear Carrie,
My next Partygate statement has to sound really sincere. Which of these convinces? 'From the bottom of my heart...blah di blah...' 'My sole wish is to serve the British people...' 'It is with a sense of great sorrow that...' etc etc.
Demagoguia hic hac hoc,
Boris

Apr 18, 2022

Dear Mogg,
Far be it from me to suggest that the people crossing the Channel are not human but this Rwanda Project has certainly brought into the open folks who think refugees are not really human beings. Do you think these folks will vote Tory?
Focus pocus gruppo,
Boris

Apr 19, 2022

Dear Mogg,
Let's run with 'I didn't know it was a party. I was busy/muddled/convalescing or just good old Boris'. The cake was just like Matron's 4 o'clock treat just as Persephone ate the Golden Fleece.
Alimentarium embargo,
Boris

Apr 19, 2022

Dear Brandon,
Very kind of you to compare Partygate to a speeding fine. You are to be commended for your cheek! I believe

the Indians have a word for it: 'chutzpah' and you
certainly have it in spadefuls as did Hercules when he
cleaned out the stables.
Versus pepperoni,
Boris

Apr 19, 2022

Dear Mogg,
I will emerge from the House like Horatio from the Tiber,
victorious and exultant, the victor cludorum, with laura
leaves coiled into my hair. No one will put a glove on me
and I will stride off to India like Cleopatra's asp.
Pyscho ludicrus,
Boris

Apr 19, 2022

Dear Mogg,
What do we know? What do we not know? What do we
not know of what we know? What do we unknowingly
know? What do we knowingly unknow? These are deep
thoughts, Moggy, that only a fine leader of men can dare
to have. Come to mine for cake later?
Catatonic catastrophe,
Boris

Apr 19, 2022

Dear Carrie,
I am bloated from eating Humble Pie to a level beyond
the most grovelling of grovels but Boris the Brave shall
ne'er be beat. I say to the browbeaters: know ye not
greatness? For ye look upon it. Btw - bloody good bash
it was too, eh?
Deportio deportiorum,
Boris

Apr 20, 2022

Dear Nadine,
Great point you're making about music helping people to
live well. That's why the last ten years have seen music
cut back in schools. Joining the dots, Nadine!
Gloria in excelsis me,
Boris

Apr 20, 2022

Dear Raab,
Get this guy off the Today programme quick! He's one of
ours and he's smearing himself with doodoo.
Devastatio chaos,
Boris

Apr 20, 2022

Dear Mogg,
Hah! Welby! Hah! BBC! Bloomin' 'eck I'm getting good at
this dead dog, cat whistle thing. One word from me and
the pigeons scatter like the Harpies flew off when Plato
dropped his plate. What? Am I to be victimised for a 50
quid fine?!
Crucifixo tragedia,
Boris

Apr 20, 2022

Dear Mogg,
Did you catch my PMQ gag about Starmer, calling him
Dr Who stuck in a time warp? Bloody good, even though
I say so myself. One pedant pointed out to me that the
time warp locks you into the present not the past. Did I
get that wrong, then?
Pedestria in orificio,
Boris

Apr 20, 2022

Dear Mogg,
Don't leak this, but to be honest, I don't bloody know
what I did or did not say about the BBC. I just thought
that the best thing to do was tell Starmer that he'd got it
wrong. Truth: does it matter? Probably not.
Polenta gelato,
Boris

Apr 20, 2022

Dear Queen,
It may turn out that I am unable to continue in office. I
would be most obliged if you could indicate to me that
should this eventuality coming to pass, you would
refuse to accept my resignation. Might I suggest that
this would be your duty?
Fossa ultima,
Boris

Apr 21, 2022

Dear Mogg,
What the boneheaded commentators don't realise is
quite simply that I don't have to go. They can scramble
about getting all frothed about this or that code but, it all
comes to nought if I stay put. Hah! I am like the
unstoppable Icarus.
Cumulus limbo,
Boris

Apr 21, 2022

Dear Mogg,
Pretty sure I'm going down well in India. I've shown how familiar I am with India by telling them that I know that Sag bhaji is cauliflower. If you were here, you'd learn something from my easy way of chatting with foreign people.
Credo lassi,
Boris

Apr 22, 2022

Dear Mogg,
Did you hear me putting out that Diwali bit? I am so hot with this foreign relations stuff. And I'll be returning to Blighty laden with the Maharajah's treasure - a trade deal! All my own work. Resign? Moi? Never!
Tiara pro dolmio,
Boris

Apr 23, 2022

Dear Mogg,
We're going for one syllable words in our slogans again. Only way to get through the thick skulls of them out there. (Don't let on that I think that!) Get it done. Gets things done. We do it. We can do it. Get the deal done. Do the deal. Hah!
Platypus populus,
Boris

Apr 24, 2022

Dear Mogg,
Some snivelling rats are leaving the ship (which is not sinking, I hasten to add). What perfidy. Was it not Mark

Antony himself who stabbed Caesar even as he rode
into Persepolis? I am the bull who is saved by the public
at the correira.
Salvatio lavatio,
Boris

Apr 24, 2022

Dear Mogg,
Did you do philosophy? I confess I'm struggling with the
notion that I could be unaware that I was breaking a rule
that I had devised. Was Euclid aware that Archaeopteryx
sat in a bath and displaced the milk he was bathing in?
Tractatus laxativo,
Boris

Apr 24, 2022

Dear Mogg,
Haven't had a chance to give you gratters on your LBW
analogy for my not knowing that it was a party I was at.
Slight prob in that whereas a batsman can't see if his leg
is aligned with the wicket or not, I could see the cake.
Logicalis excremento,
Boris

**An ardent supporter of Brexit, Steve Baker told the Prime
Minister that he should resign because he had misled parliament
over the investigations into Partygate.**

Apr 24, 2022

Dear Steve Baker,
Your phrase 'orgy of adulation' to describe my
colleagues' behaviour is out of order for two reasons 1)
it's disrespectful, 2) I do phrases like that, not you, 3) you
are guano. You'll appear in my next novel as a newt
drowning in his own slime.
Pre mortem,
Boris

Apr 24, 2022

Dear Zellinski,
I know you're a bit busy at the mo, but could you do me
the favour of penning a quick testimonial? What I have in
mind is a paean to Boris, the man who has stood at your
side on the Western Front like Hadrian with Alexander at
the Wailing Wall.
Lola tombola,
Boris

Apr 24, 2022

Dear Mogg,
I think that now is the moment we should create a Boris
War Room. We need a bloomin' great mahogany table
covered in Airfix model tanks which C-in-C Boris moves
over papier mâché Ural Mountains, each one marked
with Russian and Croatian flags.
Hummus in aldi,
Boris

Apr 24, 2022

Dear Mogg,
The advantage of me calling a General Election is that
none of the perfidious gang would dare try to dislodge

me in the midst of a campaign. I would outwit them yet again, as they plod along in their moralising bog like Aphrodite and the spider.
Ex lax hex lax,
Boris

Apr 25, 2022

Dear Mogg,
Thankfully the great British people are being protected from the villainy of the Sue Gray Report. Is there a way that it can be buried in the archives at Kew? Do you think I could slap a 100 year non-disclosure edict on it?
Embargo enlargo,
Boris

Apr 25, 2022

Dear Mogg,
Confidential: can we contact Argentina via the back door and see if we can engineer them to land a few of their troops on a sheep farm in you know where, just as Augustus landed in Britain? Then I send in the fleet and I become Churchill.
Commando solutio,
Boris

Apr 25, 2022

Dear Mogg,
I see that little Micron has been elected. Loving the news reports saying 'France is divided'. Hah! When I was elected I, of course, united the nation: Scotland-England, city and country, toffs and proles, suburbs and slums...all mine.
Rex pecs,
Boris

Apr 25, 2022

Dear Sue Gray,
I would like to propose a private confidential meeting, 'in camera' as you legal chaps like to call it. I think if we have a little tete a tete, head to head, we could iron out any awkward wrinkles that might have washed up on the beach.
Verbatim berlusconi,
Boris

Apr 26, 2022

Dear Mogg,
I'm working to the rule that the longer it takes for Sue Gray to publish her execrable 'report', the less the great Boris-loving British public will care about what it says. Hah! I will leap free like Diogenes in the Colosseum.
Placebo in placenta,
Boris

Apr 27, 2022

Dear Lord Geidt,
You are a shining light in a miasma of mediocrity matched only by the depths of Hades ruled over by sullen Bluto. Your judgements are like arrows shot from the quiver of Bacchus. May you stay long in your post to the benefit of us all.
Benedictus rictus,
Boris

Apr 29, 2022

Dear Mogg,
Oh who's for the gibbet now? I see my friends at the Mail have dug up that sanctimonious Starmer was boozing his bum off with the Lady Rayner. Tu quoque, as

Socrates would have said. I'm safe, worry ye not,
Moggo.
Scapula in sugo,
Boris

Apr 30, 2022

Dear Mogg,
As I sip my tea, I ponder it's only a 't' that separates the
words 'immoral' and 'immortal'. I, as you know, will be
immortal. Others - tawdry and untruthful - are immoral.
But I will soldier on just as Cupid battled against
Boadicea.
Fiasco al fresco,
Boris

May 1, 2022

Dear Oliver Dowden,
You have done great work today seizing the narrative
from the socialists pointing out their secret and
insidious plan to create a Lab-LibDem coalition.
Coalitions are as heinous as the Rome-Sparta one
under Odysseus.
Anathema amnesia,
Boris

May 3, 2022

Dear Mogg,
I told you me doing GNB was a bad idea. Totally unfair
questioning. How was I supposed to have heard of
Lorraine Kylie? Ask me who did Brutus kill and I'm there
with Oedipus...first to the buzzer. And all that stuff about
poor people. Oh please!
Caviti profundus,
Boris

May 3, 2022

Dear Mogg,
I will tell the Ukrainians this is my finest hour. I am seventh time lucky like the Ronnie O'Finnegan of the battlefield, just as Plato finally defeated the Goths. Please sort some optics of me in my War Room with Netflix models of Spitfires.
Victoria toria,
Boris

May 4, 2022

Dear Mogg,
Wasn't it Great Tebbitt who said that people without jobs should get on their bikes? I, of course, introduced bikes to London and it occurs to me that if people are moaning about fuel bills, why don't they get on their bikes to get warm?
Pedalo in narnia,
Boris

May 4, 2022

Dear George,
I can't be the first person to call you Useless Eustice but it was clearly a mistake to put you up for the Today programme and Kay Burley. Your burble about inflation was even worse than me and I know less about economics than my socks.
Media prohibitio,
Boris

May 4, 2022

Dear Mogg,
I think I'm breaking through. I'm really convinced by my
interviews. I think I look sincere, I sound measured and I
am full of wise words so if I think this, I know the public
think that too. For didn't Alexander follow Caesar into
Rome?
Perspex in portfolio,
Boris

**Local council elections were held across the country. Many
saw them as a chance to show disapproval of the government.**

May 5, 2022

Dear Mogg,
This is my day. People flock to the booths to vote for me
just as Rome voted for Narcissus. The British people
know that only I can save them from socialism and
people in dinghies.
Caffo nero,
Boris

May 6, 2022

Dear Mogg,
We have Starmer on the ropes. Plod is now investigating
Beergate. One-up to the serried rows of blue, eh? 'Even
the ranks of Gascony could scarce forbear to cheer...'
Doesn't matter if he's guilty or not, it takes the pressure
of me!
Gastro detritus,
Boris

May 6, 2022

Dear Mogg,
When these local election thingies are in, we need a clear line of defence: a Stentorian Guard to grasp the metal. You with your witty quips and common touch with the public are the man to do it. Say not the struggle port availeth.
Tossa in fossa,
Boris

May 6, 2022

Dear Carrie,
Post-electiones, my dear, it's not looking as ticketty-boo as I would have liked it. The constant media bias against me is beginning to show. What do they want? Titian's The Boy David? I am, like Charles 1, 'warts and all'. That's why people love me.
Pox populi,
Boris

May 7, 2022

Dear Mogg,
Poor old Labour. Some of them are still blaming Corbyn. With a bit of luck they'll still be blaming him in 2050. And as long as they do, so will we! They give us all our best lines - eg 'no money left!' Ha-ha. We print money. They moan they ran out!
Max cola,
Boris

May 7, 2022

Dear Mogg,
As Phoebus rises in the west and morn in russet-mantle clad steps o'er the dew of yon high western hill, so must

we reflect on this minor setback in the road to freedom, prosperity and war. Remember, Mogg, the banks know best.
Chaos in fusilli,
Boris

May 7, 2022

Dear Mogg,
If I was pessimistic, I'd see the results from Scotland, Wales and Northern Ireland as a harbinger of the Union falling apart but then I listen to self-basting Zahawi oozing oil into every creaking joint and I relax in the aroma of my own wisdom.
Fracturo cactus,
Boris

May 7, 2022

Dear Mogg,
Several of our council leaders who've lost seats are blaming me. They will be silenced and crushed just as the Carthaginians crushed Caesar. I am the election wunderkind as the French put it. This is a temporary glitch in the road to glory.
Insomnia in nandos,
Boris

May 8, 2022

Dear Mogg,
How tiresome is the situation in Northern Ireland? Is there some way that NI could be severed from the rest of the island and floated out to the Atlantic? Serious suggestion. Check with the geologists, please.
Hibernia in rectum agonia,
Boris

May 8, 2022

Dear Mogg,
I think I am surrounded by an aura - not just of greatness but of invincibility. I glow in the gaze of the public and when challenged by circumstance or ignorant tribunes, my aura rebuffs them just as Claudius overcame the Wooden Horse.
Mascara in candelabra,
Boris

May 9, 2022

Dear Raab,
Good show yesterday. Beware the trap of wanting Starmer's neck on the block for any reason that his leftie lot will demand the same of me. We are in the same cleft twig that Oedipus was when he accused the fox of deserting Romulus.
Rota pro semolina,
Boris

May 9, 2022

Dear Mogg,
The flakes are up in arms over a shortage of hay fever pills and blaming us! Just blow your dribbly noses, as Matron always said. The woke talk as if the Tories are to blame for their snot. Hah! The slings and arrows of outrageous Neptune, eh?
Harissa in linctus,
Boris

May 9, 2022

Dear Michelle Donelan,
I know you're one of my ministers but have we met?

CLXXXIX

Fine words from you: 'Starmer will have to search his soul.' Even the great poet Hercules found that hard so Starmer is sure to flunk, eh?
Pus in curriculum,
Boris

May 9, 2022

Dear Mogg,
So Starmer is trying to call my bluff, eh? Hah! What he and his entourage don't realise is that in the event of him resigning I shall simply say I, unlike him, have work to do. The nation calls, just as Rome called for Midas.
Peristalsis in spasm,
Boris

May 10, 2022

Dear Priti,
You're absolutely correct in saying the people at fault over your excellent Rwanda plan are lawyers. You call them 'specialist' but you and I know they are cosmopolitan, metropolitan elite, cultural marxists as was Mark Antony in Athens.
Extra tapas in lacuna,
Boris

May 10, 2022

Dear Rishi,
Glad that you and I are totally clear that letting middle and low income people have more money is bad. They just spend it! We need very high income people having more money so that they will invest and make more money for themselves.
Midas et Croesus correctus,
Boris

May 11, 2021

Dear Rishi,
I have no idea what 'levelling up' means or what we can
do to do it. You must give me some blather to say for
when a needly journo asks me. I'm busy saying we can't
spend our way out of things while saying we are levelling
up. How? Urgent.
Vesuvius in rectum,
Boris

May 11, 2022

Dear Gove,
You were supposed to be going out there this morning
putting a veneer of usefulness on the empty jug of the
Queen's Speech. Instead, you've been doing cabaret
rhetoric like Venus in the Acropolis. You're finished.
Vacuum thespia,
Boris

May 12, 2022

Dear Mogg,
I don't know what Truss is on about re the Northern Irish
Protocop. We have to keep our eyes on levelling up, up,
up. Seize the time, or as the great Scots poet Gerald
Manly Hopkin put it, 'I caught this morning, morning's
bunion...'
Carpe diadem,
Boris

May 12, 2022

Dear Carrie,
I think we must prepare for the reign of King Charles. I'll
be PM alongside a leftie bloomin' King. He'll blather on

about organic mushrooms and 'Save England's Hedges'
while I'm busy levelling up. My aura of invincibility will be
undermined.
Coma in brocoli,
Boris

May 12, 2022

Dear Mogg,
I see Nato as moving towards becoming global. If we
initiate this project, then it would be a logical outcome
for me to become its head. I've shown that I have these
leadership qualities in the way I'm winning the war in
Ukraine.
Pimento sub scrotum,
Boris

May 12, 2022

Dear Truss,
Seems like Ireland is being difficult again, but then
they've been difficult for centuries. My plan is to work on
getting the Irish to vote for an Irexit. We should plant
Farage and Mogg in Dublin to start an Irexit Party.
Erin in taxi,
Boris

May 12, 2022

Dear Mogg,
Plod says that they've issued 100 fines for our liquid
work sessions. My lips are as ever sealed just as
Odysseus's were when tied to the mast so that he
couldn't hear the Sirens. If needs be, I will pay and
soldier on levelling up.
Allegra abba pro gloria gayna,
Boris

May 12, 2022

Dear Piers Morgan,
Do you think you could see a way to starting a campaign along the lines of Free the Downing Street 100? Of course, this request has not come from me and you will claim it as your own in the name of liberty. Level up!
Mendacius confucius confusio,
Boris

May 12, 2022

Dear Rishi,
The economy is shrinking. Because people aren't buying stuff apparently. Anything to do with them having less money because their fuel bills are going up? Remember, we can't spend our way out of trouble so we can't help people with the bills. OK?
Comprehendo nil,
Boris

May 12, 2022

Dear Nadine,
Could you ask the TV people to do recipes for poor people? How to make cake out of seaweed, how to bake acorns. I think this would help level up. Let's get things done, let's get the seaweed cake made.
Nausea ad nauseam,
Boris

May 13, 2022

Dear Suella,
Bravura Braverman on QT! Surrounded by leftists, you put in the good fight for law, justice, truth, honour and, most importantly, me. How good to see the top legal

eagle in the land defending our right to party party. No
Achilles knee there!
Fido defensor,
Boris

May 13, 2022

Dear Mogg,
The woke gang are objecting to good people on our side
recommending that the wasteful 'poor' tighten their
belts and eat more lettuce. Our ancestors were hunter-
gatherers. We're here thanks to their nuts and berries.
Just tell'em to cope.
Physiognomi stuffus,
Boris

May 13, 2022

Dear Rishi,
Have you seen my civil service plan? Everyone hates
civil servants, so let's sack'em and bung the recouped
dosh at pensioners or whoever it is the woke say are
poor. I worked this out on my notes for a book I'm
writing about Caesar or Nero or Zeus.
Abacus supremo,
Boris

May 13, 2022

Dear Mogg,
The brilliant thing about my plan to sack civil servants is
that it makes 90 thousand people poor overnight. That
means less competition to get into fee-paying schools
or the best hotels. Level up, Mogg. Level up!
Impecunio comedio,
Boris

May 13, 2022

Dear Mogg,
Have to admit this Northern Ireland thingy has got me
beat. Why did no one tell me that there was going to be
Brexit bother about the bloody border? Did you ever
point out to me that Ireland is in the EU? The Guardian
Knot tightens.
No via exit,
Boris

May 13, 2022

Dear Dowden,
Jolly japes in Hertfordshire. No need to go into very-
sorry mode! The point is we Conservatives know how to
have fun. The public see that's what's special about us.
Play hard, work hard. It runs through our veins like the
River Tiber in Athens.
Apologia upmias,
Boris

May 14, 2022

Dear Zahawi,
You really are emerging as one of our best ever
Education ministers. Today's press on your calling for
Oxbridge to be 'proud of private education' is exactly
why tax-payers pay your salary. Tilt towards those who
can pay, say I. Level up!
Ave maria cari,
Boris

May 14, 2022

Dear Mogg,
If civil servants go on strike over the planned
redundancies, we will crush them just as Caesar used

elephants to crush Hannibal. No more good old Boris.
There's nothing the nation would love more than to see
us smashing feather-bedded jobsworths.
Cruella de vile,
Boris

May 14, 2022

Dear Zahawi,
At long last, someone is sticking up for Eton. For years
now, I've faced criticism, mockery and oppression for
the fact my father had the foresight and cash to send
me to the best school in the land. For that, I have been
persecuted!
Victimosis osmosis,
Boris

May 14, 2022

Dear Nadine,
I'd be obliged if you could send me a note for what to
say about the Cup Final which I believe is on today. It's
vital that I sound like a man of the people as well as a
great commander in chief on the Russian steppes as
was Plato.
Dodo in perpetuiti,
Boris

May 14, 2022

Dear Suella,
We at war with leftie lawyers. They are a pustule on the
body politic. What do they think the law is for, if it isn't
for those in power to use it? If we say, 'Clear off to
Rwanda,' so it will be, just as Lysistrata booted out Nero.
Verba deo verba meo,
Boris

May 15, 2022

Dear Mogg,
I had a dream last night...there was a boat and Priti was loading people on board. The boat was going to Rwanda. I looked closely to see if I could recognise anyone. I did. It was Sue Gray. Priti was loading Sue Gray on to a boat to Rwanda...
Assista mamma mamma,
Boris

May 15, 2022

Dear Nadine,
Had a bit of a blast last night and missed Eurovision. I can't fully read your memo but yes, I will put out a statement shortly on congratulating Sue Ryder. Was it on the BBC? If so, can you look into selling it to Elon or Dido?
Lubricato amigos,
Boris

May 16, 2022

Dear Mogg,
Now the world will see my greatness as I take unilateral action over the Northern Ireland Protocop. We are Great Britain and international agreements are just bits of paper. I will say, 'Did Zeus have paper?' Hah! What will they say to that?
Rolex in isthmus,
Boris

May 16, 2022

Dear Mogg,
Did you see me wielding a bit of jargon today? 'Hybridity'! Hah! Just as they expect me to whack'em

over the bonce with a Latin epigram I sneak in a bit of modern stuff. I'm like Circe - one moment a woman, the next a pig.
Fanta in solar plexus,
Boris

May 16, 2022

Dear Rachel Maclean,
You're a walking wonder. More hours! Absolutely! The British public are lazy sods: work harder, you lot! And Norman was right: get on yer bikes! Since Brexit, we need fruit-pickers. Get rich: pick fruit. Be like Jason: find the Golden Floss!
Tofu sub sofa,
Boris

May 17, 2022

Dear Mogg,
I know what's going to happen soon: some junior tick is going to corner me in a studio and ask me how much is a loaf of bread. Can you give me a short list of basics - very short list, or I won't remember it - of cost of milk, bread, pâté etc?
Surplus nasturtium,
Boris

May 17, 2022

Dear Truss,
It's fine for you to be bullish, but don't start getting ideas that you're going to be Number One. I have no intention of moving out no matter what Sue Gray chucks at me. I am as immoveable as the rock of Sisyphus.
Mango data,
Boris

May 18, 2022

Dear Mogg,
Bloomin' hecketty heck, I think I've worked it out. No need for a border in the Irish Sea, nor on the island of Ireland! We put it in the air, floating and hovering about like the Minotaur when he flew towards the sun.
Rodeo pro azalia quango,
Boris

May 19, 2022

Dear Mogg,
I am so so bored with all this cost of living talk. On and on it goes about bloomin' household bills, eat or heat, the price of fish. I didn't come into politics for this dreary stuff. Yawn yawn. I'm a leader of men, not a bloody debt collector.
Calippo in asda,
Boris

May 20, 2022

Dear Mogg,
O tra-la, Plod has wiped my slate clean. We will of course make sure that gongs find their way towards those who have performed their national duty by relieving me of this unfair burden. Easy lies the crown that wears the head, eh?
Piccalilli in camera,
Boris

May 20, 2022

Dear Mogg,
As Dickens wrote, 'What larks, Barkis, Pip is willin'!'
They're going to name the lowly worms of the Uncivil

Service who frolicked in our 'Déjeuner sur L'herbert' at Number 10. Jolly hard fromage on them, eh! (Trying not to larf.)
Delirium tremendens,
Boris

May 20, 2022

Dear Mogg,
Potential trap ahead: fined and disgruntled Number tenners, going to the press with eyewitness claims that I was at the jollies. Was Brutus at the death of Caesar? No. You may have to give them a going over in the cricket pavilion.
Listeria in cranium,
Boris

May 21, 2022

Dear Mogg,
Some hack has dug up that I had a secret meeting with Sue Gray. Stitch up, shout the sneerers and smearers. On and on. This feels like the never-ending labyrinth where the monster Manatee lurked.
Motto grotto,
Boris

May 21, 2022

Dear Mogg,
One big thing I learned at Eton was when one of the Masters found someone had stolen chocs from the Tuck Shop, I dived in quick with, 'It was Bradstock Minor, sir,' and he got it in the neck. Hah! Watch me next week with the Gray Report...
Plebs in executiones,
Boris

May 21, 2022

Dear Mogg,
The speech I will give to the top Uncivil Servant will be:
"We all have to make sacrifices and on this occasion
you're the one making it. You lose your job so that I can
keep mine. I'm sure this will be a consolation to you."
Concretum excrementum,
Boris

May 21, 2022

Dear Mogg,
How might I bask in the glow of the Queen's Jubilee? It's
vital that we accrue what we can of the national
feelgood factor. Investigate whether I can wave from the
balcony of Buck House just as Pontius Pilate rode into
Jerusalem on an ass.
Platinum aspidistra,
Boris

May 22, 2022

Dear Zahawi,
Great job today keeping the hacks at bay trying to find
out who set up my meeting with the shark-in-waiting
Sue Gray. It's keep-it-in-the-scrum time. No loose balls
out to the wingers and I'm in the clear.
Casa nostra hero,
Boris

May 22, 2022

Dear Mogg,
We've cracked this cost of living probby: it's simple, we
tell people to work harder, longer, more often or do more
jobs. Great message because it tells people who've got

enough money that poor people are poor because they're lazy.
Parlio faeces,
Boris

May 23, 2022

Dear Simon Clarke,
You were in fact talking cock when you said that Sue Gray set up the meeting with No 10. No 10 set it up. You'll have to wipe the egg off your face later. Or, if you're like me, never! Hah! Let the charivari run on, I say and sod'em all.
Scrotum totalis,
Boris

May 23, 2022

Dear Mogg,
Oh the foolish Fourth Estate thinking they can second guess me! Who do they think they are? Cassandra when she rightly predicted the Fall of Nostradamus? It's simple: whatever Gray the Frightful One says, I stay put.
Don immobile,
Boris

May 23, 2022

Dear Mogg,
Some leaky sod has snitched on me and sent the odious ITV News a pic of that blast we had during lockdown. Sanctimonious gobs need shutting, methinks. Life's too short to dwell on mild errors, don't you think, Moggy?
Peccadillo circus,
Boris

May 23, 2022

Dear Cummings,
You are lower than the asp that killed Mark Antony. I
need say no more. Carrie was right to have booted you
out but I confess, even I didn't conceive that you could
drink so deeply from the cup of green-eyed revenge.
Eterna herpes,
Boris

May 23, 2022

Dear Carrie,
Ring that Scotsman at the Spectator and see if he's got
any gaps. I think the stormy sands of time are gathering
in the sky. Check the back door is off the latch. Even
Plato had to leave the Colosseum.
Extra curricula problema,
Boris

May 23, 2022

Dear Mogg,
Seems that some have spotted that someone got a fine
for the party in the ITV photo but I didn't! What's the
prob? I'm Boris. I am not cut from the same cloth as
other men. Of course the Met know and respect that just
as Perseus respected Medusa.
Colossus pisces,
Boris

May 24, 2022

Dear Mogg,
What people don't understand is that I dashed in, raised
a glass and dashed out again. I am a master dasher. No
one dashes as fast as I do. I'm fleet of mind, flexible of

foot. Hermes, god of war, was no faster.
Festivo festo infesto,
Boris

May 24, 2022

Dear Shapps,
Your appearances today should emphasise that the
Elizabeth Line is a glorious tribute to what I've done for
London. It's fine that Her Majesty is celebrated but it
might have been more appropriate if it had been named
the Boris Line.
Nomenclatura transit,
Boris

May 24, 2022

Dear Mogg,
I will explain to the House later today that the photo
they're all whingeing about shows me warning everyone
that they really must stop this illegal gathering right
away. I'm holding the glass aloft saying, 'You can't sit
about drinking THIS!'
Vino veritas upmias,
Boris

May 24, 2022

Dear Mogg,
The Times is running with the idea that I strong-armed
the frightful Sue Gray to try to get her to drop this bloody
report. Did I? Did I? I just told her to bloody not publish it.
What's wrong with that?
Tibia fractura,
Boris

May 24, 2022

Dear Mogg,
The squirt who's replaced the delectable Laura K is
actually doing a pretty good job. He seems to have
found some of our chaps who are backing me and he's
running with the idea that my Hightorian Guard will
stand firm.
Dulce et decorum vest,
Boris

May 24, 2022

Dear Shapps,
You are an officer and a gentleman. Thank you so much
for saying that the red box was evidence that it was a
work meeting. Keep this under your hat: in fact there are
no docs in the box. It's stuffed with snifters and
sausages.
Prioritas sybaritico,
Boris

May 24, 2022

Dear Mogg,
How long did it take for the sneaks to start snitching, eh?
Laura K (Et tu, Laura?) has crossed some palms with
silver and what-d'you know - former Boris-o-philes have
squealed! Never trust a servant! It's why Circe killed her
pigs.
Evidentia in plentia,
Boris

May 24, 2022

Dear Mogg,
I created a culture of fun. I was the fun-loving king.
Working for me was one jolly after another. Do we want

killjoy leaders who look like they live off vinegar? I may have been in charge of Lockdown, but I was bloomin' well against it.
Hedonisticus pissticus,
Boris

May 25, 2022

Dear Mogg,
What do you think of my 'humble' shtick? I am soooooo humbled! As if! But hah! Mrs Bloggins in the Red Wall is going to fall for it. Didn't Cleopatra fall for Achilles? Move on, move on, ye little people.
Fraudio officio,
Boris

May 25, 2022

Dear Mogg,
Well that's all blown over. The backbenchers still love me. They're all turning up on the media posing with dour and thoughtful looks but they loved me in the 1922. I'm partic proud of my 'I take responsibility' line. It means nothing! Hah!
Bogus giganticus,
Boris

May 25, 2022

Dear Mogg,
The joke is that if bloomin' Labour had got caught out like this, we'd've been giving them both barrels with how they had betrayed the 'sanctity of high office', failure of 'moral leadership', 'lost the trust of the British people'.
Hypocrisia immensicus,
Boris

May 26, 2022

Dear Barclay,
Just heard you on Today prog. You deserve an Oscar for
backing me up on my absurd line about not knowing
that 200 revellers were rocking up at No 10! My word is
'vindicated'. Hah!
Veni, vidi, vindicato!
Boris

May 26, 2022

Dear Bacon,
Excellent work! It's time we turned the tables on those
bloody NHS workers - getting all the bloomin' credit
yawn yawn. Of course loads of them having parties in
the broom cupboards. Let's have a Panorama on that,
eh?
Accusatorio torio,
Boris

May 26, 2022

Dear Mogg,
The point is that we do regard the Great British Public as
mortals of a lesser kind. I could swear we are of a
different genus. The rules we make are for the GBP, not
for us - just as Augustus made the rules for
Agamemnon not Menelaus.
Superior anus,
Boris

May 26, 2022

Dear Carrie,
Good you're keeping out of sight. I've been in a bit of
scrape: I think of it as being in trouble with Matron.
Anyway, I ate lashings of humble pie but had my fingers

crossed! Hah! And we've hit back with dosh for the lower orders.
Confectionari bambini quids,
Boris

May 27, 2022

Dear Rishi,
Good job yesterday. But don't kid yourself you're number one. Say your piece and then step off the stage, OK? Everything you say and do should be to ensure that the light shines ever brighter on me. 'Through a glass darkly,' as Timon of Athens said.
Ego in cuppo,
Boris

May 27, 2022

Dear Mogg,
Keep an eye on mutiny on the bounty. One or two snivelling little weeds are turning against their leader. You need to go out there and break a few legs. Starmer is a dangerous Bolshevik who would seize power like Narcissus overthrew Augustus.
Omnibus terminus,
Boris

May 27, 2022

Dear Mogg,
Have you heard of a girl band called ABBA? Carrie adores them, plays them all the goddam time, actually, especially at parties. I gather they're on tour. Can you wangle me tickets. A box preferably and I can keep out of view.
Incognito incontinent,
Boris

Dear Mogg,
With the whole ghastly Partygate matter I haven't
written a word of this Shakepeare book jobbie. Thought I
could hire someone but don't have the readies. Could
you touch Rish and see if he could lend me a bob or
two? Didn't Hermes support Virgil?
Bardus retardus,
Boris

Dear Mogg,
That wretch Paul Holmes (who he?) has resigned
(resigned from what?). He must be seeking a one-day
headline. He lists 'real ale' on wiki as one of his
recreations. Can you upgrade that to something dodgy
and leak it to the Telegraph?
Narcotico phonio,
Boris

Dear Mogg,
The sneerers and jeerers are concocting a theory that
I'm fiddling the ministerial code to save my skin. Not
fiddling, Moggy - adjusting. And giving more power to
the one person who can decide these things: the PM.
Me!
Trumpo hero,
Boris

Dear Mogg,
On the odd occasions I see my brats, (ah! uneasy lies

the crown that heads the bear) - I help them with their
Latin prep. Conjugations this week. (I love conjugations.)
Vomo, vomis, vomit...etc etc.
Detritus in numeralo X,
Boris

May 29, 2022

Dear Mogg,
We need to work on ways to make this Jubilee be more
about me. Suggestions to me by close of play.
Sin dulci jubilo,
Boris

May 29, 2022

Dear Mogg,
Some uncouth youth spotted me yesterday and
shouted, 'I can't believe you're still the f***ing Prime
Minister.' I whispered back (sotto voce) 'Neither can I.'
Indeed, probs no one can believe it. Hah! The Power of
Mirage.
Blotto voce,
Boris

May 29, 2022

Dear Mogg,
I see the rumour mill is claiming I'm bringing back
Imperialist measures. Hah! Do they know my mind
better than I do? Don't answer that one! Stops'em
talking about ABBAgate and ToryPartygate though!
Con toto cum urino,
Boris

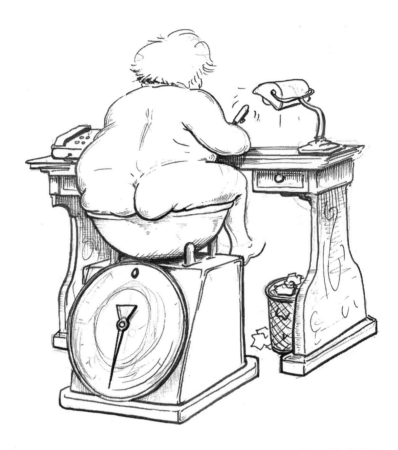

May 29, 2022

Dear Carrie,
Not sure where you are at the mo but just warning you
that the wolves are closing in on the ABBA party. I can't
remember who was there (that'll be my excuse) because
I was blotto before I arrived. Delete all missives.
Panic manic,
Boris

May 30, 2022

Dear Mogg,
Haven't heard from you for a few days. Not seen you on
TV or heard you on radio. Odd. You're usually the first to
be defending me. Can you give me a call? Send a text?
Just to confirm you're fully on board? As on board as
Odysseus on the Argo.
Squitto in toga,
Boris

May 30, 2022

Dear Rishi,
There was something unpleasantly relaxed about the
way you stood at the Despatch Box, dishing out dosh to
the plebs. Remember: you were fined too, Mr
FixedPenaltywallah. Don't get above yourself or you'll be
sent to the North-West frontier.
Chapati in tesco,
Boris

May 30, 2022

Dear Mogg,
I've got it! We not only spray the Red Wall with olde
Imperialist measures - how about we bring back ration
books? Blitz spirit...all in the same boat...and at the
same time, we cut consumption, cut inflation.
Nostalgia reflex genius,
Boris

May 30, 2022

Dear Mogg,
How many times do we have to say that the matter is
closed? There is no more to see. (There is, but the point
is we're saying there isn't.) Btw, our guy said he refused
to deny that a party took place. Go on TV and deny that
he refused.
In via excrementum,
Boris

May 30, 2022

Dear Mogg,
Who is Jeremy Wright? Have I ever met him? I'm
guessing he's an aggrieved remoaner, hoping to get in a
dig in order to curry favour with his remoaning
constituents. We march on in yards not in bloomin'
millilitres.
Coladangelo causa resignato non abba,
Boris

May 31, 2022

Dear Mark Francais,
Your staunch support of the old Imperialist measures is
stiffening the sinews of the Red Wall. The weak-kneed
waverers lodging their rebel missives to Mr 1922 have to
be crushed just as Persephone crushed Virgil.
Tara ma salata,
Boris

May 31, 2022

Dear Mogg,
Oh look at the miserable weeds pushing their way into
the limelight: the Leadsom harridan, Hague the
vague...What traitors they all are. My Hightorian Guard

will defend me just as the ranks of Tuscany defended
the bridge against Horatio.
Pistachio inferno,
Boris

May 31, 2022

Dear Priti,
Magnificent news: while 1000s are stranded at the
airports, you've chartered a flight to take small boat
invaders to Rwanda. What a great Brexitty message!
Beware wrecking by cultural Marxist north London
metropolitan elite lawyers tho'!
Concentratio camporum,
Boris

May 31, 2022

Dear Mogg,
The sands of time have taken wing and dripped into
fate's jaws. Destiny's horse has cooked its goose yet see
how Neptune rides the clouds. My number has come up
on future's alphabet, and we know not whither the owl
swims.
Hic nonni nonni no,
Boris

May 31, 2022

Dear Lord Geidt,
What I sent you before is just official waffle for public
consumption. Take this as my real missive. You can say
what you want but in ultimo, I decide. You are my
servant. Remember: even Horace had to clean the
Augean stables.
Occludo physiognomio,
Boris

Jun 1, 2022

Dear Nadine,
Your appearances on the media defending me are
worthy of Cicero when he appeared in Aristophanes'
plays. You are a beacon of light in the river of shame.
You know better than anyone that I am loved. I'm not
sure by whom, but I am, aren't I?
Quart in cubit,
Boris

Jun 1, 2022

Dear Mark Franglais,
At least the Greenwich Time Signal never went metric,
eh? Imagine if there had been ten bloomin' pips! The fact
that we didn't ever succumb to such nonsense is a
testicle to the common decency of the Great British
Public.
Comprendo zero,
Boris

Jun 1, 2022

Dear Connor Burn,
I'm not seeing things very clearly this morning, we were
celebrating the solstice last night. Or was it the full
moon? Anyway, can you clarify this Protocol thingy? Did
we sign it? What is the GFA? What is a Yellow Order? Or
is it Orange?
Tempi ultimi,
Boris

Jun 1, 2022

Dear Mogg,
I told Mums knot I can't resign as I'm full steam ahead
on levelling up. You and I should be a levelling up

committee to devise some red hot levelling up ideas.
Didn't abysmal Heseltine have some idea to do with
parks. Shall we try that?
Elevato per bognor regis,
Boris

Jun 2, 2022

Dear Nadine,
Can you give me some coordinates on this - am I in any
way disreputable? All I ever read in the papers or see on
TV are people implying that I am a wrong-doer. Am I to
be driven out of the Pantheon like Hubris the god of
wheels?
Gastro ente ritis,
Boris

Jun 2, 2022

Dear Priti,
How right of you to invoke the joy of the Jubilee in an
effort to quell the rebellion by the turncoats and traitors
in our ranks. You are like Pallas Athene rising to save
Rome from the Persian hordes. My next step: abolish
the 1922 committee.
Cystitis linoleum,
Boris

Jun 2, 2022

Dear Mogg,
Have you noticed the ranks of backbenchers who used
to shout my name from the rooftops now lurking in the
shadows like Judo, God of the Underworld? We need
more lead for their pencils: bring back olde Englishe
measures like Fahrenheit and Amps.
Compos dementis,
Boris

Jun 3, 2022

Dear Mogg,
Am a little disconcerted with the Jubilee jollities in that there has been hardly any focus on me. Luckily, there's still a couple of days in which you and my other faithful cohorts can scrape together some splendour for me.
In jubilo gloria gaynor est,
Boris

A service of thanksgiving for the Queen's reign was held at St. Paul's Cathedral. Some video clips appeared to record booing as Boris Johnson and his wife went up the steps to the entrance.

Jun 4, 2022

Dear Priti,
I've had time to reflect on the disgraceful scenes outside St Paul's. In the light of this, you need to draft a Bill to ban booing Conservative ministers. We're on a downward slide up a mountain of disorder.
Tyrannosaurus in asda,
Boris

Jun 4, 2022

Dear Nadine,
Can you up your use of 'woke'? It's excellent as scattergun abuse of anyone who doesn't buy into our Rwanda-Police Bill-AbbaParty type policies. If you were ennobled, what title would you like? Dame Dorries? Lady Nadine?
Propa ganda non stoppa,
Boris

Jun 4, 2022

Dear Priti,
Could you look into the feasibility of making living in
North London a criminal offence? Where do the liberal
metropolitan cultural marxist woke elites come from? N
London! Quod erat remonstrandum.
Correlatio ad absurdum,
Boris

Jun 4, 2022

Dear Priti,
Could you draw up a list of places and events where we
can guarantee that I won't be booed? My appearances
should be bathed in bonhomie which I can return to
grateful onlookers with my natural charm.
Saliva cosi fan tutte,
Boris

Jun 5, 2022

Dear Mogg,
A lot of media crap talk about storm clouds brewing,
anger mounting in the shires (blah blah). Who do they
want? (Gove?) Didn't I say I was 'humbled' (hah!)? We
need a new policy to shut them up. What about algae
farms? Monorails? More grammar?
Non secateur,
Boris

The Platinum Jubilee 'Party at the Palace' was staged outside
the gates of Buckingham Palace. Lee Mack was the compere.
He made a joke about gates and parties. Stephen Fry's contribution also riffed on the woes of the Conservative government.

Jun 5, 2022

Dear Nadine,
Am hoping that you will produce some of your superb,
barbed wit to deal with last night's Fry and Mack
debacle. I felt like Paris at the Judgement of Helen.
(That's from Greek mythology.) Is Mack north London
woke? Slack bob.
Turismo cortina previa,
Boris

Jun 5, 2022

Dear Rupert,
Please be so kind as to excuse me for taking the liberty
of writing to you without having first received a letter
from you. May I remark that your media outlets appear
to be not as sympathetic to our cause as we have
traditionally expected them to be?
Exit,
Boris

Jun 5, 2022

Dear Carrie,
As Othello said, 'Tomorrow and tomorrow and tomorrow
creeps in this pretty pace...' And as the Mammas and
Daddas sang, 'Monday, Monday'. I fear our sojourn at
Numero 10 may be nudging endwards. All foreseen by
Virgil in the Odyssey, I fear.
Ignominio dustbinnio,
Boris

Jun 5, 2022

Dear Mogg,
This weekend hasn't turned out well. I was pretty sure I'd
get a Jubilee bounce, with the populace showing their

CCXIX

love for me, which would echo through the Westminster bubble like Emo and Narcissus. Why don't we make it the 2022 Committee?
Taxi de Nero,
Boris

Jun 5, 2022

Dear Mogg,
We're going with health and housing. This is the right to buy hospitals and cutting waiting lists for beds in houses. This is big, levelly uppy stuff, people seeing Brexit dividends coming home to roost. We're getting the wotsit thingy done.
Pacino in serpico,
Boris

Jun 5, 2022

Dear Mogg,
We are re-running the end of Roman rule in GB when Perseus was hounded out by the Gorgons. They won't know what they got, till it's gone - that's Abba. We are mariners crying out in the storm at the start of Twelfth Night, 'We split, we split!'
Veruca in cranium,
Boris

Jun 5, 2022

Dear Carrie,
Isaiah Berlin said it all: 'There may be trouble ahead/But while there's moonlight/And music and love and romance/Let's face the music and dance.' Great philosopher, great song-writer, speaking to me and you through his work.
Con sardino diminuendo,
Boris

Jun 6, 2022

Dear Mogg,
No matter what Sir Braham Gravy says, I will win. I will
win. Meanwhile, Sajid is my Brutus, standing by Caesar,
hitting the buttons: 'challenges', 'delivery', 'getting on
with the job', 'on track'. Superbly programmed.
Subsidens sub gluteus,
Boris

Jun 6, 2022

Dear Chief Whip,
The way we rustled up support at Eton was grab
waverers by the collar, lug them off to the cloakroom
and given them a dead leg. If that didn't work, we
debagged them and painted their goolies with cold
custard. Do your democratic duty.
Genitalia calamitia,
Boris

Jun 6, 2022

Dear Mogg,
I've been talking to Biden about just how much hardware
we can chuck at the Ukrainians without Putin blowing us
all up. I explained this is all about headlines. I
desperately need 'Boris Sends in the Big Stuff', 'Boris
Saves Ukraine'.
Suicidi universali,
Boris

**A confidence vote was triggered early on Monday morning
after more than 54 Tory MPs (15% of the total) submitted no-
confidence letters to Graham Brady, the Chair of the 1922
Committee.**

CCXXI

Jun 6, 2022

Dear Mogg,
I will win tonight. I don't have to resign. What's the worst
that can happen? John Minor telling me to fetch my
coat? Malcolm Rifkind babbling on to me
incomprehensibly? Pah! I am just as the Elgin Marbles
are: forever stuck to the Parthenon.
Adhesio permanentus,
Boris

Jun 6, 2022

Dear Carrie,
The spirit and message of the classic Winona Ryder
song, 'Stand by your Man' is a salutary reminder of one's
obligations, don't you think? A model for us all is surely
the great Grant Shapps, a veritable dog in his devotion to
me.
In desperatio elasto plasto,
Boris

Jun 6, 2022

Dear Raab,
You're so right when you tweet that I got the big calls
right like 'securing life-saving vaccines'. V. glad you kept
quiet about me going for Herd Immunity in the early
days of the pandemic! Hah! We lost a few thou bods
then, eh? Whoops!
Annihilatio massificatio,
Boris

Jun 6, 2022

Dear Nadine,
You saying it would be wrong to get rid of me 'while we're at war with Ukraine' was so on message. You're a beacon of hope in the fire of despond; a shining light in the teeth of despair. You are as trustworthy as the Mona Lisa was to Nero.
Prima donna kebab,
Boris

Jun 6, 2022

Dear Mogg,
If matters come to pass in an undesirable way, I will retire to update Edward Burke's 'The History of the Decline and Fall of the Roman Empire' but all about me instead. Then as Michael Collins sang: 'Take a look at me now', so will I.
Polyfilla in pesto,
Boris

Jun 6, 2022

Dear Mogg,
Either way, this is last dance saloon now. If I lose, it's curtains. If I win, the Red Wall red necks get me in the cloakroom and tell me no more jollies, no more dropped balls. I'll be their prisoner, like poor Polyphony in Hades.
O detritus! O bidet!
Boris

Jun 6, 2022

Dear Carrie,
I am Victor Lidorum (thats's king of the lido - the Romans played games on the beach and whoever won,

won a crown made of lorries. I learned this stuff when I was up. O yes, 'up' means at Oxford.) Anyway, for the time being we're back in numero X.
Ry vita brevis,
Boris

Jun 6, 2022

Dear Nadine,
You are quite right, it's a remarkable and resounding victory for a great man. As you said, 'once more into the breeches!' and I shall do just that. The Prime Ministerial trouser awaits!
In nomine spiritu tancti,
Boris

Jun 7, 2022

Dear Mogg,
I think it was Plato who said that in the face of bullets, make yourself a moving target. Every new misdemeanour the traitors and backstabbers ascribe to me, diminishes the chances it'll be a bullseye. Hah! I am untouchable. Bash on, Moggo!
Tango san Pellegrino,
Boris

Jun 7, 2022

Dear Mogg,
We hit back! I want names now. Who are the traitors? If I had my way, they'd walk the corridors of Westminster wearing a badge displaying their treachery to the world. Shame shall be our shield. (Draw up a list, Moggo. I want lists.)
Stasi in anglia,
Boris

Jun 7, 2022

Dear Mogg,
They talk of a Pyrrhic victory. What know they know of
the Classics? Pyrrhic was a great general, husband and
father. In fact, he was such a great husband, he married
five times and Pyrex dishes are named after him.
Coca in cerebellum,
Boris

Jun 7, 2022

Dear Mogg,
The sins of omission are long remembered but the sins
of commission soon fade. My minor piccadillies will sink
beneath the surface like feathers in the wind. My next
book will be 'From Sinner to Saint'.
Santa fanta,
Boris

Jun 8, 2022

Dear Mogg,
As I said, today and henceforth, I will be drawing a line
under Partygate. Whenever anyone mentions it, I'll draw
a line under it. Am irritated to see that others are not
drawing a line under it. More line-drawing needed,
Moggo.
Pre posterus bast ardus,
Boris

Jun 8, 2022

Dear Mogg,
Oh the hurrahs as I entered the chamber today! As the
great poem goes: 'Even the ranks of Muscovy could
scarce forebear to cheer...' I've been absolutely clear

about this: nothing will stop me being PM unless
something stops me being PM.
Impetigo in hydrangea,
Boris

Jun 8, 2022

Dear Mogg,
Some timely leaking has let the press know that on
Thurs I announce how we will bring to an end the
ghastly business of homes being in the hands of
councils, housing assocs or any authority with
obligations to the public. Yuk!
Gigantico lucre in toga privati,
Boris

Jun 8, 2022

Dear Priti,
Bravo! This is shoot-out time with lefty lawyers. How
dare they try to interpret the laws that we make! We are
law-makers not law-breakers. Hah! Look into framing a
law to make it illegal to be a lefty lawyer.
Deporto snorto,
Boris

Jun 9, 2022

Dear Mogg,
My big speech today! It's about everything everywhere.
All the stuff. All of it. And it'll be really levelly uppy. All
over the place. Hah! It's my big comeback. I'm Icarus
when he flew back from the sun to a hero's welcome.
Magnificat aristocat,
Boris

Jun 9, 2022

Dear Priti,
We really have to ramp up the fight against small boat
people and lefty lawyers. The Red Wall love it. It's like
feeding seals to sharks. We are like the Romans, who
were the true rulers of Britain, when they repulsed the
Normans.
Historico testiculi,
Boris

Jun 9, 2022

Dear Rishi,
We're so right to tell workers they can't have more
money to pay for higher prices. We have to tell them that
for us on top just to stay where we are, they have to
have less. Time to tighten their boats, we're all in the
same belt.
Marcs comprehensit,
Boris

Jun 9, 2022

Dear Mogg,
Have you seen the speculation about who could replace
me? Easy Q to answer: no one! I am irreplaceable.
Everyone else is mediocre. Or damaged goods! I rise
above them like the Colossus of Roads. And as Joe
Cock sang, 'The road is long.'
Ricotta in anaglypta,
Boris

Jun 9, 2022

Dear Rishi,
Your job is to tell the people we're doing all we can to

make them better off while we're doing all we can to make them worse off. It's called profit and loss. We profit, they lose. C'mon Rishi, talk big, act mean.
Duo tongua,
Boris

Jun 10, 2022

Dear Mogg,
Send memo to Birbalsingh: it's not my job to be a role model to inner city oiks. The press pack have forgotten about Partygate. We've given them stack loads of pudding to fork through: right to buy revolution etc (sozz can't remember the rest).
Milcov amnesia,
Boris

Jun 10, 2022

Dear Priti,
Great result in the court today: so we really can ship the Rwandans to Rwanda. That'll teach'em to come in their small boats, eh? Did you come in one like that? Hah! And the woke think we're fascists! As if!
Greatus Britiscus trafficus,
Boris

Jun 12, 2022

Dear Mogg,
In Jan '21 HM Govt re Rwanda said: "We remain concerned by continued restrictions to civil and political rights and media freedom." This means that we'll never find out what happened to the people we're stuffing on board planes. Win win!
Principia crapissimus,
Boris

Jun 13, 2022

Dear Mogg,
Cornwall is superb. If only all Britain could be Cornwall.
I've dumped the new Protocol thingy on Truss! Hah!
Mind you, if she does well, I've left the back door open
for a Truss coup. Remember how Socrates seized
power.
Dyspepsia in taverna,
Boris

Jun 13, 2022

Dear Truss,
If you get asked any BS q's about Rwanda, just tell'em
that their methods of dealing with wrongdoing are
'robust but fair'. Remember: the UN is full of woke twats
who have no jurisdiction over the UK. Even Sophocles
had to tell Hadrian to get lost.
Costa cofi,
Boris

Jun 13, 2022

Dear Mogg,
I've said to LBC's Nick Bugatti that our changes to this
darned Protocol thingy are 'relatively trivial'. I've got this
absolutely dead on right. Mind you, I find most of the
crap that crosses my desk relatively trivial!
Ars longa vita breville,
Boris

Jun 13, 2022

Dear Priti,
We've done it. Stuff'em on a plane without a law to say
we can do it! Executive decision - so no bother from

CCXXIX

Parliament! Yessss! And God knows what'll happen to them when they get to Burundi, eh? We're looking good, Heston.
Detesto asylum,
Boris

Jun 14, 2022

Dear Mogg,
I've just had a dream I was in a criminal gang; I was clamping down on it; I looked closer - hah! - the gang was the Bullingdon Club, I was there and we were smashing up some stuff in the street. Bloody hilarious. Like Caligula in the Odyssey.
Finalus solutionus,
Boris

Jun 14, 2022

Dear Mogg,
Two messages today: Rwanda is so terrible it's a deterrent. Rwandan is so nice, it'll be a terrific place for these refugees to live there. The hacks won't spot the difference between these statements.
Testiculi contradictori,
Boris

Jun 14, 2022

Dear Mogg,
I play a game with the brats. I butter a slice of toast, hold it out in front of them and say, 'This is called the "Ministerial Code".' They then shout, 'We're Lord Geidt. Don't eat it Daddy!' and then I sit on it and fart. Bloody hilarious.
Politicus seriosus,
Boris

Jun 15, 2022

Dear Mogg,
So we are at war with the Trotskyist lawyers of
Strasbourg. Then am I Horatio on the bridge facing
Hannibal. But did his elephants get across? No more
shall the Nazi lawyers of Strasbourg. Hah! And Partygate
fades in the morning dew.
Aero transit fiasco,
Boris

Jun 15, 2022

Dear Mogg,
The sight of a great British plane grounded by Euro
fanatics will stiffen the sinews of erstwhile rebels in our
ranks. They will return to the fold, chastened by their
moment of disloyalty, ready to boil the lance of Euro
domination.
Quaffo pro blotto,
Boris

Jun 15, 2022

Dear Mogg,
The great thing about us going on and on about our
independent Rwanda deterrent is that no one can prove
that it's no such thing! It's not as if traffickers are all over
the media contradicting us. So we can just bang on and
on about it.
Inertia perfecta,
Boris

Jun 15, 2022

Dear Mogg,
Good point being made by some of our more loyal
colleagues: who elected these European judges? Hah!
No one. Whereas our great British judges are elected, of
course. Aren't they? (Not my subject!)
Cranium in rectum,
Boris

**Boris John's ethics adviser, Lord Geidt resigned. He told MPs
that there was a "legitimate question" over whether Boris
Johnson broke ministerial rules over Partygate.**

Jun 15, 2022

Dear Geidt,
Your resignation causes me no embarrassment
whatsoever. I outlived your predecessor and no reason
why I shouldn't outlive the next or the next. The raisin
d'etre of me and my government is that we define
what's ethical, not toffs like you.
Ultimus chapterus,
Boris

Jun 16, 2022

Dear Raab,
You got massacred on the Today programme this
morning. Don't worry about it. I only put you up for doing
that stint because they'd rip me to pieces too. Sorry,
chum. You're not sharp-witted enough to cope but no
one else would do it.
Formaggio concretio,
Boris

Jun 16, 2022

Dear Mogg,
Who do you advise we wheel out to rubbish Lord Sheidt?
We need someone who can talk as if this stuff is all
rather trivial and beneath them. We need to hear disdain
and aloofness in their voice. And a smattering of
constitutional bollock. Ideas?
Pronto contra,
Boris

**The acronym ECHR stands for the European Convention on
Human Rights. It was set up before the European Union after
World War 2 and the abuses of human rights during that con-
flict. Suella Braverman held the position of Attorney General.**

Jun 16, 2022

Dear Suella,
Can you look into how we can get out of the EHCR and
abolish the Ministerial Code at the same time? We need
to rid ourselves of this worthless red tape, so beloved of
lefty lawyers and undercover Trotskyist Nazis.
Taurus in china taverna,
Boris

Jun 16, 2022

Dear Shapps,
I've got you pencilled in to drive the 9.15 Kings Cross to
Edinburgh.
Hei presto rapido transit,
Boris

Jun 16, 2022

Dear Mogg,
The guy who does Ethics says I'm not ethical. I could

start being ethical. Or I just get rid of the job of the person who decides what's ethical! There are now no more ethics for me to bother about. See it, say it, stuff it! Excrementum vincit omnia,
Boris

Jun 17, 2022

Dear Lynton Crosby,
May I thank you for attending our Cabinet meetings. No way are you an intruder or outsider. Your incisive way of reminding us to gather support through urging people to turn on others is massively helpful.
In inferno,
Boris

Jun 17, 2022

Dear Mogg,
A whole raft of people out there are talking about the EHCR as if it's part of the EU! Or that it's the same as the ECJ! With a wave of that sort of opinion behind us, we can walk out of there like Persephone walked out of Hades: forever!
Flexi exit,
Boris

Jun 19, 2022

Dear Mogg,
Am relying on you to do some judicious deflection work on this Times story abt me, Carrie and 100k per annum. And the story abt the Times story that I supposedly whacked them with an injunction. And the story that the Times pulled the article.
Pandora explosionis,
Boris

Jun 19, 2022

Dear Suella,
You must publish a redefinition of 'ethics'. It's being
weaponised against me. My definition is: what can't be
seen is ethical. If what can't be seen is exposed, it's the
act of exposure that's unethical.
Veritas berri sub taurus faeces,
Boris

Jun 19, 2022

Dear Carrie,
We're hiking through some pretty tricky white water
rapids at the mo with a story that the bloody Thunderer
has got hold of to do with that thingy that never bloody
happened anyway. Key thing: not a word to the hacks.
In junctionis super,
Boris

Jun 21, 2022

Dear Mogg,
Sorry been incommandicado but I've been in hospital
having a massive nose op (minus sinus!). My body's
ability to bounce back from disease, accidents and
operations is second to none, so it was only a matter of
mins before I was back at my disk.
Rhino wino,
Boris

Jun 21, 2022

Dear Mogg,
We won't be put off by what these Communist train
drivers say about our splendid agency men. Trains run in
straight lines. All you have to do is press a button to

make them go and another one to make them stop. I'm
going to drive one. Hah!
Nostradamus ignoramus,
Boris

Jun 21, 2022

Dear Mogg,
Remember we defeated the miners and now there are
no more miners. So will we defeat the railway workers
and there'll be no more railway workers. Doesn't the DLR
run without drivers? Hah! A master driver can sit in a
cabin in London and drive the lot.
Hornbi dublo,
Boris

Jun 21, 2022

Dear Mogg,
Press release: we're moving faster than Neptune the
God of Speed, proposed legislation pouring out of us like
wind from a furnace. My new Bill of Rights sweeps away
the EU meddlers in Strasbourg who blocked our
humanitarian plane to Uganda.
Super nova hangova,
Boris

Jun 22, 2022

Dear Mogg,
Chuffed to see that papers friendly to us are going with
the 'class war' line because there is only one side to a
class war: them against us. Scargill, Benn and Lynch
against us getting on with the job like Nero and his violin
playing.
Bogus versus bonus,
Boris

Jun 22, 2022

Dear Raab,
Great work on this Bill of Rights thingy. I heard you
sketched it out on the back of a Fortnum and Masons
menu while you were in the bogs. The lefty lawyers are
raving about it louder than when Archimedes killed
Agamemnon in the bath.
Terminatio justicia,
Boris

Jun 23, 2022

Dear Rachel Macleans,
We all have disasters. It's just that yours was on TV.
Don't worry about it. Look at me by way of comparison.
Have I had disasters? And where am I now? Still at the
very summit of the pinnacle. Or what was called in Latin,
the 'nadir'.
Spaffus gaffus,
Boris

Jun 24, 2022

Dear Mogg,
Am preparing a speech for if we lose both Wakefold and
Taverton. If some bolshie hacks have a dig at me, then
for a change my reply will be, 'I'm getting on with the
job.' Or have I said that before? But didn't Plato repeat
himself in the Odyssey?
Echo cacko,
Boris

Jun 24, 2022

Dear Mogg,
All good. Full steam ahead. Where is Taverton anyway? I

am so totes in charge. Just because little Ollie Dowden can't take the heat isn't a reason for me to pack my bags. Love Raab talking about 'head winds'. (btw what is a head wind?)
Cata stro phic cata stro phe,
Boris

Jun 24, 2022

Dear Dowden,
You always were a waste of space so your backsliding, whimpering exit won't be noticed. Mogg will deal with you in the traditional Bullingdon way and you'll have a great weekend. Don't you dare share this memo with anyone.
Manic panic in toto,
Boris

Jun 24, 2022

Dear Mogg,
Quick! Remind me: who are we sending to Uganda? Is it drug dealers? I remember Priti talking about boats. Are we putting the drug dealers in boats? That'll stuff that court thingy in Luxembourg, eh?
Lax max,
Boris

Jun 24, 2022

Dear Mogg,
Michael Howard is the latest of the old failures to try to sabotage my reign. Didn't he bring back hanging when he was PM? We will bat this away like the Cyclops sweeping aside the Minotaur.
Polli wolli doodli,
Boris

Jun 25, 2022

Dear Mogg,
I squashed the intrusive Michelle Hussein this morning
on the Today prog by putting a firewall round my
'personal life' pretending there's nothing political about
shovelling dosh or breaking rules. I am not just good at
this. I'm very good.
Ostin maestro,
Boris

Jun 26, 2022

Dear Mogg,
I can hear the mass of eyebrow-raising from the serried
ranks of woke w***ers just because I've said I'm going
for a third term. Little do they understand that I really
mean that I'm going on for EVER, Moggo. I am immortal.
Eterna nationali pustula,
Boris

Jun 26, 2022

Dear Mogg,
I don't listen to the doomsayers and soothsayers in our
midst. Of course I remember the Sage calling out to
Caesar 'Beware the Ides of Mars' but history is not a
matter of unfolding what's been shed. What's once read
is underwater.
Miasma incoherens,
Boris

Jun 27, 2022

Dear Mogg,
The soft-centred worms in our great party are quibbling
over the idea that I might go on forEVER. What's their
problem? Are they drowning in the light of my

CCXXXIX

greatness? Didn't Rome acclaim Pluto as he stood on
the bridge over the Bosphorus?
O excrementus immovabile,
Boris

Jun 27, 2022

Dear Mogg,
Expect me to be striding across the world stage rather
more in the coming months. I like to view humanity from
the lofty heights of Mount Hades rather than piffling
about with the tawdry morass of inflation, pandemics
and elections.
Pedestrian in transit,
Boris

Jun 27, 2022

Dear Mogg,
Best news ever. One of those jumped up polytechnics in
Leeds or Doncaster or Sheffield has stopped doing
English Literature. Too bloody right. Why should
northern kids get the sort of thing I got? Though mine
was of course Lat and Greek.
Non levelus uppus,
Boris

Jun 28, 2022

Dear Mogg,
Do you see me lounging about with the G8? I am a world
leader. This is my stage. If only there could be a mini-
Boris who dealt with the mundane stuff in Westminster
while I, mega-Boris manage the world. Here, all I need is
a white shirt.
Delusio ded lossio,
Boris

Jun 29, 2022

Dear Mogg,
Did you hear me out-woking the woke-ettes? I sprayed
them with talk of 'toxic masculinity'. The moment
libtards think they've cornered me, I'm outflanking them
with virtue signalling. Next, I'll mock them for being
virtue-signallers themselves!
Cynicismus bin go,
Boris

Jun 30, 2022

Dear Mogg,
If you don't want to know what's coming, look away
now. Anything anyone says is untrue. I believe in truth in
all things and this is why I attract such devotion. People
are on their knees in their adulation.
Fella tio ad sofa,
Boris

**Chris Pincher, MP for Tamworth in Staffordshire was alleged to
have groped two men at a private members club. This was not
the first time such allegations had been made. The Prime
Minister had promoted him to deputy Chief Whip.**

Jul 1, 2022

Dear Chris Pincher,
I sympathise with your predicament. God knows, many
of us have been caught with the proverbials round our
ankles whether we were tanked up or not. Strictly
between me and you, I don't think you needed to go
down (as it were) for this.
Pantes in flagrantes,
Boris

Jul 2, 2022

Dear Mogg,
Did you know about Pinchy? Come to think of it, did I
know about Pinchy? Maybe you know what I knew about
Pinchy. How am I supposed to remember the
peccadilloes of every backpincher? I'm busy in the War
Room winning the war with Ukraine.
Mysteriorum sub toga,
Boris

Jul 3, 2022

Dear Mogg,
The chickens are coming home to roast: Ireland and
Germany in a pincer movement surrounding Albion with
their anti-Protocol crap. But we are the Antarctic
Convoys of 2022. Pincer movement? Hah! All the papers
care about is Pincher movement.
Amnesiac paranoiac,
Boris

Jul 3, 2022

Dear Mogg,
We need some brand new stuff this week, to get the
hacks on to how bracing and innovative we are. I know
it's all a bit Dom-com but getting things 'done' was good
is always good. What are we getting done next week?
Harvests? Fireworks? Bridges?
Distractorum forum,
Boris

Jul 4, 2022

Dear Mogg,
This week I will have the hacks strung out trying to prove
the unprovable: what I knew or didn't know about Pinchy
when he was blotto or not. Hah! Even I don't know what I
knew or didn't know about what I knew or didn't know
about Pinchy.
Debris in cranium,
Boris

Jul 4, 2022

Dear Mogg,
Do you get the impression that every Monday the press
dump some new mess on my doorstep? Why me? I'm
just a decent, jolly, kind guy making sure that people
around me have a good time. Why does it keep going
wrong? But I will fly on and on like Icarus.
Ego in sugo,
Boris

Jul 4, 2022

Dear Mogg,
Number 10 has made it absolutely clear that I knew that
I didn't know that I knew about Pinchy. Punchy knew
that I didn't know that I knew that I didn't know too.
Matter closed.
Clarificatio obscuratio,
Boris

Jul 5, 2022

Dear Mogg,
Am I not in office? Who are these sages and wiseacres
who think they can wish me out of office with a flourish

of the pen? The quitters are creatures of the dusk:
midges who flee at daybreak. I am unvanquashed.
Solo polo,
Boris

Jul 6, 2022

Dear Carrie,
Things getting a teensy bit hot here but I'm steadying
the truck. Swift moves to staunch the leaves and great
new faces willing to step up to the Plato. The vagabonds
of doom may well sing out their fanfares but let's see
where the dice fails.
Scrotum collapsus,
Boris

Jul 6, 2022

Dear Mogg,
I'm off to bed now. It's been a bit of rollertoaster today,
eh? If a few more traitors leave overnight, delay
informing me until after I've wolfed my whack of
bangers and Potatoes O'Brien swilled down with a shot
of Johnnie Walker.
Dementia dyspepsia,
Boris

Jul 6, 2022

Dear Mogg,
They're resigning so fast I can't keep up with
replacements. We need an outsourced supply system:
Ministers for Hire. Dido could run this. Keep an eye on
Nadhim Zahari. We lost the North West Frontier,
remember.
Credibilitas sub zero,
Boris

Jul 6, 2022

Dear Carrie,
To be absolutely honest (don't say that'll make a change!), I don't think things are going quite as smoothly as I hoped. A mix of traitors, liars and careerists are seeking to slay me just as Priam slew Achilles. Your hero will defy them.
Interminablo finale,
Boris

Jul 6, 2022

Dear Nadhim Zahari,
There you were on the radio this morning saying you were 100% behind me and, 10 hours later you're 100% against me. You are like Janus the two faced god who gave us the name for February. You lot make me sick. I have plans.
Applicatio nextus jobbus,
Boris

Jul 6, 2022

Dear Mogg,
Did Chronos know he was eating his dogs? This teaches us that none of us is perfect. I am finding your silence irritating. I thought we were like the inseparable twins Pisces and Taurus. You will rot in hell for this.
Limpet ad nauseam,
Boris

Jul 6, 2022

Dear Nadine,
When the anals of these times come to be written, your undimmed loyalty will be a rock of light in the morass of

chariots. Your foresight has cut through the timeserving pastry. Arise Sir Nadine.
Mamma mia tia maria,
Boris

Jul 6, 2022

Dear Boris,
It is with great regret that I feel obliged to say that the time is fast approaching when I will not be able to continue in my role as your official letter-writer. The reason is plain: you have disappeared into your own fundament.
Comedia centrali,
Michael

Jul 6, 2022

Dear Mogg,
It's becoming clear that in the end I will have to sack everybody. This makes perfect sense because, as Churchill wrote: If you can keep your head when all about you are losing theirs and blaming it on you, you'll be a man. I am that man.
Cranium in rectum,
Boris

Jul 6, 2022

Dear Mogg,
The history books will remember me as they remember St Pauls Cathedral resisting the Blitz. I am honed granite facing fire with dignity and grandeur. I hear the country summoning me: seize the time, Boris, cargo diem.
Mentalio putrefactio,
Boris

Jul 7, 2022

Dear Mogg,
What the media hacks need to realise is that the people resigning are below the level of amoeba in the food chain. They aren't even minions. They're primeval slime in government sinecures. I am Hercules clearing the Augean tables.
De facto elvis,
Boris

Jul 7, 2022

Dear Mogg,
I saw the lily-livered naysayers quiver as I fired off that image from 'Antony and Cleopatra' - you'll have to dip your hands in blood! Hah! And we all know what happened to Cleopatra: poisoned to death in her family tomb. High steaks indeed.
Allusio bonkus,
Boris

Jul 7, 2022

Dear Mogg,
Can you draw me up a list of possibles to fill the holes left by the snakes, yellowbellies and traitors? Some will have to double up - Northern Ireland and Wales is an obvious one for that. I'll chop Zahari later, Peter Bone could fill in there.
Emergenci chaos,
Boris

Jul 7, 2022

Dear Mogg,
When I say that I've gone, that means gone in the sense of not gone. It's the marriage of opposites as the great Greek philosopher Catullus proposed. The country is calling for me to stay while toads in the media pile vituperation and calumny upon me.
Ego returno,
Boris

Jul 7, 2022

Dear Mogg,
Hark now how those who clamoured for my departure descend into foul-mouthed vilification as they reach for the crown! Only then will they realise that they have slain the calf that lays the golden egg.
Error o error in excelsis meo,
Boris

Jul 7, 2022

Dear Mogg,
Preposterous! People are suggesting I have become deluded and incoherent. Far from it. I have always been deluded and incoherent.
Consisto insisto,
Boris

Boris Johnson resigns as Prime Minister but says he will stay on as 'Caretaker' until the Conservative Party elects a new leader.

Jul 7, 2022

Dear Mogg,
I've played and replayed my excellent performance
outside Number 10 today. I was at my charismatic best.
Full of bravura and charm while working the crowd with
a sense of regret and loss. And the hacks bought it!
Absolute turnaround: zero to hero.
Volte farce,
Boris

Jul 7, 2022

Dear Mogg,
Not many people know that I am a great observer of
men - thus my allusion to 'herd instinct'. They hunted
me in packs, driven by dark innate urges. Failing to fully
catch their prey, they will now turn on themselves and
eat each other.
Anthropologica bolloc,
Boris

Jul 8, 2022

Dear Mogg,
The hacks have done - nay, are still doing - a good job. I
am 'much loved' by the Great British Public, will be
missed for my refreshing and unconventional style but
above all I got things 'done'. It all feels like post mortem
tributes, eh?
Obit excelsior,
Boris

Jul 8, 2022

Dear Mogg,
To ensure that my legacy is respected, I will write the
official biography of Boris Johnson. It will be informative,
accurate, honest and insightful, exploring the
tremendous contribution I've made to national political
life and culture.
Gloria in excelsis meo,
Boris

Jul 8, 2022

Dear Mogg,
Could you check in your dusty tomes to see if there's
anything to stop me putting my own name forward in
the upcoming Tory Party leadership contest? Following
the media tributes, my gut feeling is that I would stand a
pretty damned good chance.
Homo numero uno,
Boris

Jul 8, 2022

Dear Mogg,
My fave phrase used about me is that I delivered
'bravura insults'. Hah! That one won't go down well with
the woke crowd, forever whingeing on and on and on
about my jolly little jests about letterboxes, bum boys
and piccaninnies.
Slaggo hilarius,
Boris

Jul 8, 2022

Dear Mogg,
Appalling hoo-hah going on about our delightful refurb.
We were the custodians of Number 10 which was at the
time kitted out with frightful John Lewis curtains and the
like. I anticipated that we would be occupants until 2030,
so value for money.
Non ikea,
Boris

Jul 8, 2022

Dear Nadine,
No, it is not possible for me to guarantee that you will
have a post in the new government unless, the cards fall
in such a way that once again, I am summoned to the
greatest office in the land. Let's see how it crumbles
cookiewise.
Albion expecto,
Boris

Jul 8, 2022

Dear Mogg,
To paraphrase Lady Gaga, 'I should be so sorry...' (She
was very good in 'Neighbours' I thought.) Why are the
woke crowd whingeing about how I should say sorry?
For what? For being the most exciting, exuberant, joyful
PM this country has ever seen?
Gaga in denialo,
Boris

Jul 8, 2022

Dear Rishi,
Don't you realise you are a joke? If, as the nasty hacks
have tried to say about me, that I am muck, then you are

mucked up by my muck! You have all my supposed
drawbacks and none of my heroic gloss. Tough titties,
pal.
Homo contaminato,
Boris

Jul 9, 2022

Dear Mogg,
Could you look into your dusty tomes again for me and
check what would stop me calling a general election?
Nothing! I could say that the leadership contest was
'causing uncertainty' and that the people need a chance
to say what they want...?
Solutio megalo,
Boris

Jul 9, 2022

Dear Mogg,
I rather like the cut of this Andrea Jenkyns woman. She
displayed a certain brio in the way she dealt with the
woke crowd milling about on our patch the other day.
We need more of that feisty stuff to see off Starmer's
ragbag of communists.
Mid digit in atmos,
Boris

Jul 10, 2022

Dear Mogg,
The traitors and snakes are eating each other. Oh how
this fills my poor aching heart with pleasure! Meanwhile
whole cohorts of Borissorites beg me to stay on. As
Socrates said to Cleopatra, 'I feel the love.'
Gluteus adhesive,
Boris

Dear Mogg,
I have a dream that Her Maj summons me to hand in my resignation. I reply politely that I am with my beloved family in the heart of the home entrusted to us by a grateful nation and I'm not leaving. Eat that, Maj.
Gambit desperatum,
Boris

Dear Mogg,
The more I learn about this Andrea Jenkyns woman, the more I like her. She has what Indians call 'chutzpah', sheer good old British nerve in the face of the baying woke. Absolutely first class material to be in charge of education.
Swivello plebs!
Boris

Dear Mogg,
Of course I don't bloody back any of the snakes fighting for my job. I loathe them with every fibre of my soul. Whoever is chosen will abjectly fail and I will be called back as saviour.
Christus in Uxbriggus,
Boris

Dear Mogg,
Starmer's communists have tabled a no confidence vote. Watch the snakes: the very same backstabbers who slew me in the Forum, their togas stained with my

blood, now leaping to their feet to defend me, while I am
as pushed for cash as Midas.
Quest pro quids,
Boris

Jul 12, 2022

Dear Mogg,
Shapps has gone. See how they drop like flies. I'm wary
of Truss. She's a woman. I'm surprised you're backing
her. Was it not Cassandra who stabbed Archimedes in
the bath? Was it not Cleopatra who poisoned Socrates?
Femina equalis disastrus,
Boris

Jul 12, 2022

Dear Mogg,
This is not a leadership contest. It's a mutiny. I see that
Priti has shown excellent judgement in refusing to take
part. I surmise that she knows that I will return, just as
Odysseus returned to Britain to defeat Boudica.
Parlio per aperture anal,
Boris

Jul 12, 2022

Dear Mogg,
Might I assume that you have brokered a deal with the
excellent Truss in which she will appoint me as Ukraine
Tsar? I will sally forth on my charger to defeat the
ghastly bear (without further alienating certain Russian
friends at home).
Oligarchi amigos,
Boris

Jul 13, 2022

Dear Mogg,
Your talk of 'disloyalty' as your reason for not supporting the backstabbing Sunak is all fine but you've overlooked the fact that you have stooped to supporting anybody! They are all mutineers. As Oedipus said to Pythagoras, 'Wakey wakey!'
Mango in londis,
Boris

Jul 13, 2022

Dear Mogg,
At PMQs today, I demonstrated to the snakes on either side of me what a loss it would be if I were to be banished to the backbenches. I fill the House with the silver prose of Cicero in the Ancient Greek Assembly whether what I say is true or not.
Non departo,
Boris

Jul 14, 2022

Dear Mogg,
That Beatles song 'Ghost Town' sums up what it feels like at Number 10. All the fun and jollity I brought to its hallowed walls has evaporated and now staff skulk along the corridors like Andromeda when she was hauled off to Hades by Bluto.
Non quit,
Boris

Jul 14, 2022

Dear Mogg,
What's lower than a snake? Olympus. That's David Davis. His speech attacking me was the first crack in the waterfall and now he's backing this Comprehensive

School girl, Penny Mordant. We are sliding downwards
into the Slough of Despont.
Non evacuatio,
Boris

Jul 14, 2022

Dear Mogg,
People whinge on and on and on about the cost of living:
living costs. The clue is in the language. What does
living do? It costs. Living costs. (See, Moggo, I haven't
lost the witty Boris. Still there, eh?) So go away whingers
and pay your taxes.
Arroganto soddo,
Boris

Jul 14, 2022

Dear Mogg,
I will be the most famous backbencher ever. The House
will hear my stentorian tones ringing out as I hound the
backsliders on Brexit, the lily-livered appeasers on
Ukraine and the nitpicking killjoys on Partygate. The
future is me.
Ultra vox pro Boris,
Boris

Jul 14, 2022

Dear Mogg,
I'm looking about for a new canvas on which I can paint
my aspirations. I will probably accept being Chancellor
of Oxford University when they offer it to me. In the
meantime, I could do with being an emissary or an
equerry or an effigy of some sort.
Rambo tango,
Boris

Jul 14, 2022

Dear Mogg,
Given that in the coming months I may be a little short
on employment opportunities, I need to explore new
horizons. I was wondering if you could make an
approach on my behalf to see if I could be one of the
participants in next year's Love Island?
Dude nudo,
Boris

Jul 15, 2022

Dear Mogg,
I am being frozen out of this leadership debacle.
Remember, I am still at the helmet, steering the train of
state. I should have a queue of backbenchers at my door
seeking my counsel. Instead, nothing but calumny and
contempt. It distresses me.
De facto laxativo,
Boris

Jul 15, 2022

Dear Mogg,
Could you look into the constitutional regs on whether I
can give myself a peerage? Hah! I have a premonition of
myself as a knockabout comedy guest on Graham
Norton or Would I Lie to You? appearing as Baron Boris.
It has to happen, Moggo.
Corruptus interruptus,
Boris

Jul 15, 2022

Dear Mogg,
The Party has the weekend to ponder on the dreadful
error in making me stand down from being leader of the

Conservative Party. But - hah! - I haven't resigned from
being PM. Changing Party leader not the same as
changing PM!
Uppus yourus, succus.
Boris

Dear Mogg,
When Hercules said, 'Hier stehe ich', he meant he would
never leave the Forum in Rome even if it entailed
dragging him out. How that rings bells for me, Moggo!
The fate of the nation depends on my determination,
resilience and honesty.
In situ - non in shitu,
Boris

Dear Mogg,
Hashtag 'Bring back Boris' is trending. What does this
tell you? I duck the heartstrings of the nation, that's
what. The Great British People and I have a liaison as
firm and as long lasting as Odysseus and Calypso. As
Bond says, 'I'll be back.'
Fester in fortnum,
Boris

Dear Mogg,
The Woke are bleating about my Resignation Honours
List. Hard fromage, snowflakes! I insist I will reward the
loyal, thus securing the passage of my raft of Bills thro'
Parliament, just as the good ship Excalibur sailed
between Scylla and Chlamydia.
Multi croni,
Boris

Jul 16, 2022

Dear Mogg,
More bleating from the Woke. Inside every Wokista is a puritan killjoy. While they castigate everything that moves, we're partying, yay! Don't tell on us: we're asking people to come in Pandemic NHS fancy dress! Nurses uniforms (yum!) etc.
Immoralus arse holeses,
Boris

Jul 18, 2022

Dear Mogg,
O gawd, there's a whole lot of blithering hoo-hah about our Chequers bash. The Woke mob just won't leave it alone, will they? I am the bloomin' PM. I can do what Caesar did in the Peloppenesian Wars: do what I want! Just watch me, Wokers.
Tori histori,
Boris

Jul 18, 2022

Dear Mogg,
O ha bloody ha! The next TV leadership debate's been cancelled. It all got too heated last time, 'twould seem! Where they sow dissent, I spread harmony. The Party will turn to me once more, just as Rome turned to Cyclops.
Cobra in absentio,
Boris

Jul 18, 2022

Dear Mogg,
I had a dream that we were looking in on a cage where a nest of vipers were eating each other. But I wasn't

distressed. I was laughing in my usual hearty way. Then the vipers stopped and turned to me, calling on me to take control. Of course, I did.
O solo meo,
Boris

Jul 18, 2022

Dear Mogg,
A resounding victory: of course everyone decent and good has confidence in me. An indication that my removal is an egregious error. How they will regret it! Just as Aristotle regretted slaying Pontius PIlate. We must learn from history, Moggo.
In shitu profundus,
Boris

Jul 19, 2022

Dear Nadine,
Were you sloshed? Was I sloshed? Hah! Don't see how knocking back a few spritzers could have felled us! I must say you were pretty damn raucous in the Chamber though. Last days, Nadders, last days. As Marie Lloyd sang, 'Je ne regrette rain.'
Intoxico shoxico,
Boris

Jul 19, 2022

Dear Kate Hooey,
I am grateful for your tweet. As you suggest, MPs will regret their frightful bloodletting. They have lost the greatest leader to grace Westminster since Winston left us. Yet, as Abba sang, 'You don't know what you got till it's gone.'
Meo gratias,
Boris

Jul 19, 2022

Dear Mogg,
Hark the Woke mob in uproar over my aside about the execrable Lady Hale! I single-handedly fought off the tentacles of the judiciary reaching into the sanctity of Parliament. Now the mob is claiming she was going to retire anyway. Phooey to that.
Argumentum logico,
Boris

Jul 19, 2022

Dear Mogg,
Excellent moment for this Labour Party Ford Report. We must spin it as incompetents ripping each other apart in equal measure - unlike us. Takes the heat off me too!
Btw - how come Fords got involved?
Auto chassis in pesto,
Boris

Jul 20, 2022

Dear Mogg,
See how the nauseating Woke crowd quiver and quake at my mere mention of the deep state! This tells me that the Woke ARE the deep state: creeping about the corridors of Whitehall intent on thwarting Brexit and imposing north London elite values.
Paranoia in tesco,
Boris

Jul 20, 2022

Dear Mogg,
The reason why I said 'Hasta la vista, baby' from the Die Hard movies was because I wanted people to remember

that other great quote from the same movies: 'I'll be back!'. Subtle allusion there, Moggo. My cheery demeanour will tug on their heartstings.
Cello jello,
Boris

Jul 20, 2022

Dear Mogg,
Did you see the front bench snakes clapping me to the rafters? The very same wretches and traitors who left me lying bleeding on the floor of the Senate on the Ides of Mars. O very well might they throw their plaudits at me but they fall on deaf eyes.
O pieta me,
Boris

Jul 21, 2022

Dear Mogg,
It's come to this: I'm not on the front pages. It's a nightmare come true. I'm left sitting in the bogs googling 'Boris' on my phone and all I get is yesterday's news. Disaster akin to the Wooden Horse in Rome.
Legaci mangli,
Boris

Jul 21, 2022

Dear Mogg,
Following the lamentable assassination of Caesar (o what echoes, Moggo, what echoes!), Athens set up a triumvirate. Behind the scenes, I will propose such an arrangement: Truss, Rishi and me. Later, I will arrange for them to be shaved off.
Proto dictator,
Boris

Jul 22, 2022

Dear Mogg,
Even as I relax, basking in the glory of that tremendous
valedictory you graced me, I see that the foul media,
wallowing in their own spew, seek to bait me with the
possibility that I will lose my seat in the great city of
Uxbridge.
Veni vidi vino,
Boris

Jul 22, 2022

Dear Mogg,
I can't bear to watch the News anymore. Where the
screen used to lavish its attention on my tousled hair
and boyish grin, now it's wall-to-wall snake. Nay, it's
worse: it's two backstabbers wrestling, Brutus and
Persephone.
Mojito ergo sum,
Boris

Jul 23, 2022

Dear Mogg,
I sense a groundswell. Even as the snakes bid for votes, I
hear the call. My rumbustious no-nonsense mien
touches people's hearts. I will be like James the First
when he reclaimed the throne at the time of the
Restoration.
Cactus in rectum,
Boris

Jul 23, 2022

Dear Mogg,
Thinking about a new kind of chat show I could present:
guests come on each week but instead of me

CCLXIII

interviewing them, they interview me. This way, I show the audience my vast array of talents until, in the end the nation demands I return as PM.
Esso in honda,
Boris

Jul 25, 2022

Dear Mogg,
Every time I read a paper all I hear is Rishi, Liz, Rishi, Liz. They are Boris's children but no credit comes back. I ought to strap myself to the mast and stuff my ears with bees wax just as Circe did so she couldn't hear Odysseus.
Cornetto castrato,
Boris

Jul 25, 2022

Dear Mogg,
I've been reading the ruins: when the delightful Liz becomes PM, I think you'll find I'll be easing my glutei maximi back on to one of the Cabinet chairs. You can put the cat out, but if it turns into a dog you can't stop the dog getting back in.
Jigeri pokeri,
Boris

Jul 26, 2022

Dear Mogg,
Rishi's blown it. He'll lose his place in the Cabinet. I'll do Chancellor. Am not great at Arith but neither was Aesop, the hypotenuse guy. Delectable Ms Truss will sort. She is the Botticelli Medusa Rising from the Sea.
Samosa sub mucosa,
Boris

Jul 26, 2022

Dear Mogg,
Starmer and the Red Harridan herself are after me over
the jolly I had at Lebvedevev's Villa. How am I supposed
to remember what I promised him? I thought he was
Gareth Southgate at first. Did Cleopatra recognise
Aristotle? Am enjoying hols.
Scrotum al fresco,
Boris

Jul 27, 2022

Dear Mogg,
The smearers and sneerers at HQ are casting doubt on
the massive upsurge of support I am receiving. They say
that some Bring Back Boris petitioners aren't members!
So what? On occasions, reality has to be expanded.
Icarus rose again, as will I.
Magna farta,
Boris

Jul 27, 2022

Dear Mogg,
Am being tipped for an array of jobs that I'm perfectly
suited to: boss of NATO, Emissary to Ukraine etc. All
getting me out the house on long jollies in distant parts.
Family life has its longueurs. Why else did Oedipus fight
in the Trojan Wars?
Excessivo peppa,
Boris

Jul 27, 2022

Dear Mogg,
Did you see what Zilinsky says? He says I shouldn't
'disappear'. O ye gods, hear how the great warriors

across the seas can see the way we spurn our homegrown hero! As traitors crush me underfoot, so will Zekinsky raise me up.
Multi magnificrap,
Boris

Jul 28, 2022

Dear Nadine,
O ye wise Roman goddess Athena: you show the world how I was slain by Sunak. Our camps draw up on the battlefield with the regicides one side and you gorgeous loyalists on the other. As Winston said, 'It's the triumph of the will'.
St Pancreas defendat me,
Boris

ST PANCREAS DEFENDAT ME

Jul 28, 2022

Dear Liz,
I awoke to the sound of music and in an instant saw a
promotional video in my mind of you, Nadine and me
striding towards the camera while Joe Cocker and
Jennifer Anniston sing their hit 'Lift us up where we
belong...'. Seize the day, Liz!
Carpet diem,
Boris

Jul 28, 2022

Dear Mogg,
Protect me from whingers still cornering me with their
tales of woe about not seeing Granny during lockdown.
We've put that one to bed. Do they want me to cook a
great big humble pie every day and spend the whole
time scoffing it? I'm busy being PM.
Diddlis quat,
Boris

Jul 28, 2022

Dear Nadine,
You are so right: it was a coup. A coup d'etail as the
French say, a highly worked out coup down to the last
detail. I have been hung, drawn and quartered like
Spartacus, his head hewn from his body and left for the
crows on Southwark Bridge.
Bellus endus,
Boris

Jul 29, 2022

Dear Ben Wallis,
Lo how you stand shoulder to shoulder with me. You are
Brutus to me, Caesar. I know that you know that I know

CCLXVII

who the traitors were. The Tory Party is a united party and when Liz wins, we'll trample Sunak in the dust.
Venom in balti,
Boris

Dear Nadine,
How gratifying to see you spending your time making a stand against the ragbag of cultural marxists, and woke class warriors by defending the great Cecil Rhodes who quashed the Indian Mutiny and discovered New Zealand.
Minto imperialo,
Boris

Dear Suella,
What a moment of genius! You've put the ranks of lefty lawyers back in their bolshevik boxes and told them it's not for them say what's unlawful. That sort of thing is best left to the likes of me. And believe me, I know what's unlawful.
Parlio per orificio,
Boris

Dear JCB,
It's fantastically generous of you to be laying on this wedding bash for us, only possible now that the Pandemic is over. After all, it was no parties back then, eh? And how on the button it is with your company: I love bulldozing things.
Regulatio buggeratio,
Boris

Jul 30, 2022

Dear Liz,
Glad you're getting the support of Tom Tinhat, but watch him closely: be like Cressida who said, 'Yon Sophocles has a lean and hungry look'. Btw, may I point out that when you become PM, that Foreign Sec comes vacant again?
Quit squit,
Boris

Jul 31, 2022

Dear Nadine,
Your retweet of me as Caesar, Sunak as Plato stabbing me in the back is so on message and so brave of you to post. The woke ninnies will of course try to pull you down. Worry ye not. Liz has it in the bag. Places in Cab await both of us.
Tapioca in optrex,
Boris

Aug 1, 2022

Dear Mogg,
I'm feeling the glow - first the Bring Back Boris clamour, then my glorious wedding bash, followed by the Tigresses' fantastic victory. I missed the game. Were they any good? Give me some good quotes for who was best at the lineouts etc.
Supremo ignoranus,
Boris

Aug 1, 2022

Dear Mogg,
Mulling over my honours list. They pretty well choose themselves: heroes who've filled the Party coffers - our

lovely donor kebabs, eh? We don't need to faff about trying to find bloomin' worthies from the provinces who've run bazaars for sick kids.
Mea cuppa,
Boris

Aug 1, 2022

Dear Mogg,
I have to admit it: moments of melancholy, the sunset on my brilliant career, and I must go forth, like Icarus, and find other ways to lead my people to the Promised Hand. In the end - hah! - I was caught in an Accordion Knot.
Testes in vice,
Boris

Aug 2, 2022

Dear Liz,
Don't worry about the sums. I never did. Just come up with figures, bang them out to the hacks, everyone pores over them, social media twats claim they're rubbish but you're out there being busy, busy, busy. No one reads what the experts say.
Rictus in vacuum,
Boris

Aug 2, 2022

Dear Mogg,
Call me a scheming McAvellyian, but with the abysmal Truss about to take over, the country - nay, the world - will see the shooting star they have lost. Only then, will we see me welcomed back to ride in triumph through Acropolis.
Linctus in sphinctus,
Boris

Michael Rosen is one of Britain's best loved writers and performance poets for children and adults. His first degree in English Literature and Language was from Wadham College, Oxford and he went on to study for an MA at the University of Reading and a PhD at the former University of North London, now London Metropolitan. He is currently Professor of Children's Literature at Goldsmiths, University of London where he co-devised and teaches critical approaches to reading on an MA in Children's Literature, having done the same at Birkbeck, University of London. He has taught on MA courses in universities since 1994. He was the Children's Laureate from 2007-2009 and has published over 200 books for children and adults, including the recent bestseller 'Many Different Kinds of Love' and 'On The Move.'

Seven Arches Publishing Cartoon Competition

Have you enjoyed the cartoons in this book?

Do you enjoy drawing cartoons yourself? If so, why not send us a photo of a cartoon you have drawn? Email it to:

admin@sevenarchespublishing.co.uk

The competition is open to adults as well as children so do not forget to tell us how old you are to enable us to judge entries fairly.

If it is one of the three best cartoons sent to us, we will include it in the hardback edition of this book that is coming out in March 2023. If you are a winner we will contact you to see if you want your name added.

The cartoon can be about anyone or anything, but it must make us laugh, chuckle or smile.

The closing date is: 15 January 2023.